Biological Experiments
and
Activities
Integrating Mathematics

— B.E.A.I.M.s —

$$\frac{\partial a}{\partial t} = \frac{a^{*2}}{s_b + b} - r_a a + D_a \frac{\partial^2 a}{\partial x^2}$$

$$\frac{\partial a}{\partial t} = a^{*2} - r_b b/c + D_b \frac{\partial^2 a}{\partial x^2} + b_b$$

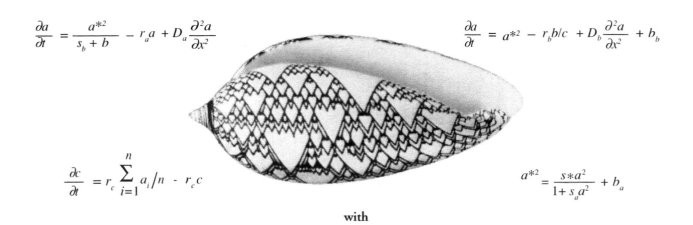

$$\frac{\partial c}{\partial t} = r_c \sum_{i=1}^{n} a_i / n - r_c c$$

$$a^{*2} = \frac{s * a^2}{1 + s_a a^2} + b_a$$

with

Stephen B. Rodecker
Chula Vista High School
Chula Vista, CA

Jim Patzold
Clairemont High School
San Diego, CA

Illustrated by
Charles Henson and Ron Garcia

Spectrum Publications
Bonita, CA

Cover Design by Ron Garcia, Ron Garcia Productions
Technical Support- Lewis J. Camp, Macintosh Consultant
Statistics Consultant - Dr. Steve Reed, San Diego State University
Prepress Assistance - Avocet Communication

About the frontispiece-- Tropical sea shells exhibit great diversity in their pigmentation and form. The pigmentation of many shells, however, shows a regular pattern formation which can be described mathematically. Pattern formation in sea shells and the algorithms used to describe these patterns provide a stunning example of biological phenomena which can be characterized using mathematics.

Pattern Formation in *Olivia porphyria*: a and b activator/inhibitor interaction; decay rate of the inhibitor is regulated by a hormone c that is a function of the total number of activated cells.

Olivia porphyria: computer-generated image by Deborah Fowler and Przemyslaw Prusinkiewicz, University of Calgary, 1992. Reprinted by permission of the authors. Image and equations from *The Algorithmic Beauty of Seashells* by Hans Meinhardt, Springer Verlag Berlin, Heidelberg, New York. 1995

Visit us on the Internet at: http://www.sciencemathlabs.com

Foreword

Oil and water, cats and dogs, biology and math.... all entities which traditionally do not mix. The science of biology, however, has undergone a revolution in the past quarter century and has evolved, so to speak, into a whole new organism. It has changed from a mostly descriptive science into a dynamic, experimental science, necessitating the application of more and more math to collect, manipulate, and analyze biological data. Students now in our classes will become the citizens and scientists of a new millennium--a new millennium which will require more science literacy of its citizens than at any point in history.

As two genuine math-phobes with a deep-rooted fear and loathing of all things mathematical, we suffered through calculus and biostatistics in college while yearning for the safe havens of our anatomy and botany labs. Nevertheless, the reality for us in biology now more than ever requires that students integrate more math into biology.

BEAIMs was written to help students apply mathematics to biology-- and do it in a way that using math in science becomes comfortable for students before they run the mathematical gauntlet of chemistry and physics. Providing students the opportunity to apply simple mathematics in biology to collect, manipulate, and analyze data lays the foundation for these later classes. While one way of performing an experiment may be recommended in *BEAIMs*, students must certainly be encouraged to try alternate experimental and analytical methods. As electronic sensors are used more and more to record data in calculator and computer based labs, students will gain increasingly accurate data to analyze. Teaching students techniques to analyze these data will remain as critical as ever.

BEAIMs is a supplementary lab text designed to augment your existing biology labs. It is intended to provide math-based biology activities and labs for the occasions when they integrate smoothly into your curriculum. We hope that *BEAIMs* enhances your repertoire of biology labs, and that it will make your teaching--and your students' learning--more interesting and rewarding far into the new millennium.

Steve Rodecker   Jim Patzold

Bonita, CA
1998

Table of Contents

Teacher Information

Teacher Background

Laboratories and Activities/Lab Data Sheets

General Topics

Genetics

Molecular Biology

Statistics

Dealing with Data

Appendices

Using BEAIMs

BEAIMs was designed to allow students to collect, manipulate, and analyze biological data mathematically. While many of the activities require a substantial amount of mathematics, none of the activities requires more than the four basic math functions, logs, or square roots. The use of calculators is encouraged to manipulate the math quickly and accurately.

Teacher Background
The first section of the book consists of Teacher Background pages. Each Teacher Background section is two pages long and consists of:
1. Purpose- The reason for doing the lab is given.
2. Objectives- What students will learn during the lab is stated.
3. Time- Approximate times are given for the Pre-lab and Laboratory.
4. Math Preparation- Any special math manipulations which students need to be aware of are noted here.
5. Lab/Activity Preparation- Instructions on solution preparation, equipment, and specialized techniques are given here.
6. Extensions- Ideas are mentioned here for students who wish to go beyond the usual parameters of the lab. *In addition, many of the labs contain procedures which could be used as the basis for open-ended science fair projects.*
7. Answers to Questions- Some answers to questions are provided. Since students will be generating their own data in the labs, answers will vary.

Student Laboratory Pages
Each student laboratory is two pages long. It consists of:
1. Prelab or Introduction- The mathematical nature of these labs requires students to work with formulas or calculations which pertain to the lab <u>before doing the lab</u> itself. By doing the Prelab problems and questions, students will familiarize themselves with the math in the lab. They will not only gain a better understanding of the lab, but they will also be able to collect, manipulate, and analyze their data much more quickly and easily.
2. Laboratory/Activity- Students follow the directions of the lab or activity, gather the data, make graphs, and analyze data.

Laboratory Data Sheets (LDS)
Each Laboratory Data Sheet is two pages long. It consists of:
1. Answer blanks- Blanks are provided for students to answer questions. In addition, blanks are provided for students to check ($\sqrt{}$) when they have read and done a step in the directions.
2. Problems- Many labs provide problems so that students can practice the math they will be using in the lab.
3. Graphs and Tables- Many Lab Data Sheets provide graphs and tables for data.

Lab Reports
The Laboratory Data Sheets can be turned in as such or can serve as the basis for comprehensive essay-style lab reports. The information from the LDS can be used to support any style of lab report. In addition, several of the labs are open-ended and can be used as springboards for **science fair projects.**

Laboratory Safety Guidelines for BEAIMs

Before starting any lab, make your students aware of any possible hazards from chemicals or equipment. A lab safety contract and quiz signed by the teacher, student, and student's parents are highly recommended as a means to preclude potential problems. Students must understand that safety guidelines must be taken seriously and are to be followed at all times. An outstanding safety video by **Insights Visual Productions** called *Safety in the Science Classroom* is highly recommended (See our Internet page.).

Specific Safety Tips

1. Check to make sure that your district permits the use of chemicals required in the labs.

2. UV Light- Students working with UV light must wear UV opaque safety goggles at all times. If they are handling samples under the UV light, they must wear gloves, as well. Exposure to the UV light must be minimized.

3. Working with *Escherichia Coli* Bacteria-- All laboratory surfaces should be cleaned with a disinfectant such as Amphyl (commercially available) or a 10% bleach solution. Hand soaps with disinfectants should be available. Make sure students are trained in proper sterile technique. Using the proper techniques when transferring or plating bacteria precludes many problems. The *E.coli* strain JM83 is recommended as it cannot colonize the human intestine or transfer plasmids to *E. coli* strains living in the intestine. Any items containing bacteria need to be sterilized at 20 lbs. of pressure for 20 minutes to ensure decontamination before disposal.

4. Working with Yeast- Although the strain of UV sensitive yeast called for in the lab is not infectious, the same precautions should be taken with it as with bacteria. Sterile technique must be used throughout.

5. The solution used in the pigment chromatography lab--Petroleum Ether and Acetone-- can be noxious to breathe. Make sure students use it under a hood or in a well-ventilated area. There can be no open flames. The test tubes must be tightly capped while the chromatography strips are running.

6. Ethidium Bromide-- Two labs call for DNA to be stained. There are a number of proprietary DNA stains on the market, as well as methylene blue, which students can use to visualize the bands in their gels. **Ethidium bromide can be used only by teachers and must be used only with permission from the district. The teacher must have been specifically trained in its use and, especially, its disposal.**

Special Equipment Needs

Most labs in BEAIMs use equipment and materials typically found in high school classrooms. However, there are several labs requiring specialized equipment:

1. DNA labs- Gel electrophoresis boxes; power supplies, light box, micropipettes, camera, specific chemicals and biologicals listed in the Teacher Background pages.
2. Bacteria and yeast labs- Wheel plating device (see page 106); 'hockey stick' (see page 106)

BEAIMs Overview of Activities

Lab/Activity	Description	Lab Skills	Math Skills
Using the Metric System	M, l, and g are used to measure popcorn.	Metric system is used to measure in m, l, and g.	Converting units within the metric system; graphing.
Scientific Notation	4 functions, metric system, and organism size in S. N.		Powers of 10, converting metric system in S. N.
Exploring Atoms	Parts of atom introduced.		Calculated number of protons, neutrons, and elec.
Measurements in Microscopy	Measurement of microscop. objects using μm.	Microscope is used to measure small objects.	Calculating field of view, determining size of object.
Surface Area to Volume Ratio in Cells	Baggies with water used to investigate SA/V ratio.	Volumes of water measured.	SA and vol. calculated, then SA/V ratio; graphing.
Diffusion in Potatoes	Effect of sugar water on potato cores.	Metric system is used to measure in m, l, and g.	Volume of cylinder calculated, graphing.
Enzymes and the Rate of Reaction	H_2O_2 and liver used to study enzyme Rx rate.	Water displacement gas trapping method.	Rate of enzyme-substrate reaction is calculated;graph.
Carbon 14 Age Determination	Age of objects interpolated from ^{14}C half life graph.		Half life of ^{14}C graphed. Age of objects interpolated.
Pigment Chromatography	Spinach pigments are investigated.	Chromatography setup, accurate measurement.	Pigment distances measured, R_f calculated.
Measuring pH in Zygocactus	Circadian pH fluctuations of Zygocactus investigated.	Mortar and pestle, pH meter are used.	Powers of 10, logarithms, graphing.

BEAIMs Overview of Activities

Lab/Activity	Description	Lab Skills	Math Skills
Effectiveness of Antibio. and Antiseptics	Antibiotics and antiseptics tested on bacteria.	Sterile technique, plating bacteria, measuring.	Analyzing size of rings of inhibition; graphing.
Serial Dilutions	Yeast grown in different sugars and serially diluted.	Sterile technique, plating yeast.	Powers of 10; graphing.
The Hardy-Weinberg Equation	H-W equation determines frequencies of human traits.	Data collection, analysis.	$p^2 + 2pq + q^2 = 1$ analyzed.
Fibonacci Sequences	Fruits, vegetables checked for Fibonacci sequences.	Data collection, analysis.	Numbers from fruits, veget. analyzed for Fibonacci seq.
Percentage of Oxygen in the Atmosphere	Germination of peas used to find O_2 % in atmosphere.	Measuring, handling chemicals.	Ratio and %.
The Ribbon of Life	Mathematical history of life on earth.		Ratio and %.
Stimuli, Senses, and Time of Response	Speed of response to light, sound, touch responses.	Measuring distance in metric system.	$t = \sqrt{2d/g}$; graphing.
Work, Power, and Calories	Number of joules, watts, and calories from exercise.	Measuring distance in metric system.	$W = Fd$; Power= Work/Time Calorie= Joules/4,184.
The Effect of UV Light on Yeast	Yeast grown after exposure to UV light.	Sterile technique, plating yeast, counting.	Graphing number of yeast colonies.
Building a Model of DNA	Students build a 25-30 m functional model of DNA.		Ratio of model to real DNA.

BEAIMs Overview of Activities

Lab /Activity	Description	Lab Skills	Math Skills
Family Genetics	Probability of children inheriting certain traits.	Data collection, analysis.	Calculating probability.
Crossing Over and Gene Mapping	Crossover freq. used to make *Drosoph.* gene maps.	Data collection, analysis.	Calculating frequency of c/o event; math. posit. of genes.
Probability in Biology	Coin tosses used to model inheritance of traits.	Data collection, analysis.	Calculating probability.
Analyzing Single Trait Crosses with $\chi 2$	Monohybrid corn cobs analyzed using $\chi 2$.	Data collection, analysis.	$\dfrac{(o - e)^2}{e} + \dfrac{(o - e)^2}{e}$
Analyzing Two Trait Crosses with $\chi 2$	Dihybrid corn cobs analyzed using $\chi 2$.	Data collection, analysis.	$\dfrac{(o - e)^2}{e} + \dfrac{(o - e)^2}{e} + \dfrac{(o - e)^2}{e} + \dfrac{(o - e)^2}{e}$
Restriction Analysis of Lambda DNA	Number of base pairs in gel bands analyzed.	Using electrophoresis, loading wells, running gels.	Powers of 10; logs, antilogs.
Effect of UV Light on DNA	Destruction of plasmid DNA by UV light quantified.	Using electrophoresis, NIH Image to quantify DNA.	DNA quantified using NIH Image graphs.
Correlations	Students correlate height with foot size.	Data collection, analysis.	Correlation formula; graphing.
The Central Tendencies of Data	Height data analyzed- mean, median,mode, range.	Data collection, analysis.	Calculation of mean, median, mode, and range.
Analyzing a Normal Distribution	Height data analyzed using a z-test.	Data collection, analysis.	Calculation of standard deviation, z score.

BEAIMs

Teacher Background Pages

Using the Metric System

Purpose:

Students will learn how to change units in the metric system and use the metric system to investigate popcorn.

Objectives:

After completing this laboratory, students will be able to:

      1. Convert units in the metric system.
      2. Measure length, mass, and volume in the metric system.

Time:

Prelab - 50 minutes with instruction about the metric system   Laboratory- 50 minutes

Math Preparation:

1. It is very useful to have students know the information in Table 1. Have them make up mnemonic devices to help them memorize one row of the table. Since all other rows are derived the same, they only need to know one row.

2. Be sure students are familiar with the simple, two step procedure to change units in the metric system.

Laboratory Preparation and Tips:

<u>Materials:</u> 250 mL beaker, popcorn, hot air popcorn popper, 10 mL graduated cylinder, metric ruler, balance, large container or bag to collect popcorn, heat gloves.

1. Use a good quality popcorn where every kernel will pop.
2. Ask students to bring in hot air poppers. With 3-4 poppers working at once, it reduces the lab time considerably.

Extensions:

1. Emphasize the interchangability of units. An interesting problem to pose to students: Ask them if they were given a <u>meter stick,</u> how could they find the <u>mass</u> of an object?

Answers to Questions:

1. The meter is based on 1/ 10,000,000 of the distance between the equator and north pole. The liter is based on a cubic decimeter. The kilogram is the mass of a liter of water at standard temperature and pressure.

2. The metric system is based on 10.

3. nano= .000000001; micro= .000001; milli= .001 ; centi = .01; deci = .1

4. deka = 10 ; hecto = 100 ; kilo = 1000

5.   a. 73.5 cm = .735 m   c. .0045 dl = .00045 l   e. 23,758 mg = .023758 kg

      b.1.45 hm = 14,500 cm   d. 34.69 dkg = 3469 dg   f. .000034 kl = 3.4 cl

                  g. 378 mL (water) = 378 cc which weigh 378 g.

Laboratory- Using the Metric System to Investigate Popcorn

6. - 16. = √

17. Experimental results

18. Experimental results

19. Experimental results

20. Experimental results

Scientific Notation

 p65

Purpose:

Students will learn how to manipulate the very large and very small numbers used in science with scientific notation.

Objectives:

After completing this lab, students will be able to:

1. Convert numbers from standard notation to scientific notation and vice versa.
2. Multiply and divide numbers in scientific notation.
3. Manipulate metric system measurements in scientific notation.

Time:

Prelab- 50 minutes;   Activity- 50 minutes

Math Preparation:

1. Review powers of 10 with students. Explain how to multiply and divide using scientific notation.

2. Explain that metric system measurements are based on 10, so they can be manipulated easily in scientific notation.

Activity Preparation and Tips:

Materials: Pen or pencil; calculator optional

Extensions:

1. Students can look up the sizes of many more organisms and compare them.

Answers to Questions:

1. a. 3.4589×10^2 d. 8.4736×10^4 g. 2.3004×10
    b. 3.4×10^{-4} e. 4.72×10^{-8} h. 9.83×10^8
    c. 3.45×10^{11} f. 2.94728×10^5

2. a. 24,900   e. 452
    b. 64,500,000   f. .0000389
    c. .00000000000528   g. .0000000349
    d. 3,270,000   h. .0000489

3. a. 1.2478×10^{10} e. 7.18×10^{-3}
    b. 3.4656×10^9 f. 1.229×10^{-3}
    c. 2.023×10^{-2} g. 3.128×10^{-12}
    d. 1.152×10^{-3} h. 1.02×10

4.   a. 4.5×10^{-4} dm   e. 3.88×10^{-3} m

         b. 4.7×10^{2} mm   f. 5.6×10^{-3} mm

         c. 2.8×10^{-3} kg   g. 8.3×10^{-6} g

         d. 3.4×10^{5} l   h. 2.7×10^{11} km

5.

Object	Size in m in S.N.	Object	Size in m in S.N.
Carbon Atom	2×10^{-10}	Largest Blue Whale	3.353×10^{1}
Human Height	1.67×10^{0}	White Blood Cell	1.5×10^{-5}
E. Coli	2×10^{-6}	*T. Rex*	1.52×10^{1}
Tallest Tree	1.12×10^{2}	AIDS Virus	9.0×10^{-8}

6.

     a. *E. coli* is $\underline{2.22 \times 10^{1}}$ times longer than an AIDS virus.

     b. A blue whale is $\underline{2.0 \times 10^{1}}$ times longer than a human being.

     c. 1 million AIDS viruses lined up would be $\underline{9 \times 10^{-2}}$ m long.

     d. A white blood cell is $\underline{1.66 \times 10^{2}}$ times longer than an AIDS virus.

     e. A human being is $\underline{8.35 \times 10^{9}}$ times longer than a carbon atom.

     f. The blue whale is $\underline{2.2 \times 10^{0}}$ times longer than *T. rex*.

     g. The circumference of the earth is 39,000 km at the equator. How many people would it take to span the circumference?   39,000,000m /   1.67m = 2.335329341 $\times 10^{7}$ people

     h. The human body is composed of 11% Carbon. For every 12g of C there are 6.023×10^{23} atoms of C.   How many atoms of C are there in a person with a mass of 50 kg?

50 kg x 1000 = 50,000 g   x   .11 = 5500 g of C / 12 = 458.3 units of C x 6.023×10^{23} =

         2.76×10^{26} atoms of C in a person weighing 50 kg.

Exploring Atoms   *Teacher Background*

Purpose:
Students will learn about protons, neutrons, electrons, elements, ions, and isotopes.

Objectives:
After completing this activity, students will be able to:

      1. Distinguish between neutrons, electrons, and protons.
      2. Draw and label an ion, an isotope, and a neutral element.
      3. Calculate neutrons from atomic number and atomic mass.
      4. Use the Periodic Table of the Elements.

Time:
Introduction- 40 minutes   Activity- 10 minutes

Math Preparation:
1. Discuss with students that since the charge on an electron is negative, when an atom loses an electron it becomes positively charged, and when an element gains an electron, it becomes negatively charged. Give examples with the Periodic Table where students know the atomic mass and the atomic number, and have to calculate the number of neutrons.

Activity Preparation and Tips:
<u>Materials:</u> Periodic Table of the Elements, pencil or pen

1. Either hand out or make available a Periodic Table of the Elements.

Extensions:
The fusion process produces new elements in a star. Most stars start with H-H interactions which produce helium [(1 proton (H) and 1 proton (H) = 2 protons (He)]. Helium (2 protons) and helium (2 protons) fuse to form beryllium (4 protons); beryllium (4) and helium (2) fuse to from carbon (6). All naturally occurring elements beyond hydrogen in the universe are produced during fusion reactions.

Answers to Questions:
1. Matter is anything which has mass and takes up space.

2. Solid- definite shape and volume; Liquid- definite volume but no fixed shape; Gas- no fixed shape or volume.

3. See drawing in student section.

4. Most of an atom's mass is located in the nucleus.

5. An element is a substance which can not be broken down into a simpler parts.

6. Elements are made by the fusion process in stars.

7. 25 elements are found in living things.

8. Only 4 elements account for 96% of living tissue--C, H, O, and N.

9. Elements are organized in The Periodic Table of the Elements.

10. A different element is produced when a proton is added or deleted from the nucleus.

11. Drawing must show an atom with more or fewer electrons than the number of protons.

12. Drawing must show an atom with more or fewer neutrons than the stable configuration shown in the Periodic Table of the Elements.

13a. Isotope   13b. Ion

Activity- Using the Periodic Table

14.

Element	Protons	Electrons	Neutrons
Hydrogen	1	1	0
Gold	79	79	118
Carbon	6	6	6
Zinc	30	30	35

Measurements in Microscopy Teacher Background

Purpose:

In this lab students will learn how to measure microscopic objects in micrometers (µm).

Objectives:

After completing this lab, students will be able to:

1. Convert µm, mm, and m.
2. Measure and then calculate the number of µm across the low and high power field of vision of a microscope.
3. Calculate the approximate size in µm of an object under the microscope.

Time:

Prelab- 20 minutes   Laboratory- 50 Minutes

Math Preparation:

1. Explain or review for students how to change units in the metric system.
2. Explain how to calculate the high power field of vision under the microscope.

Laboratory Preparation and Tips:

<u>Materials:</u> Compound microscopes with high and low power, clear plastic ruler with mm gradations, piece of paper for drawings, 4 prepared slides per group, calculator, 250-400 mL beakers for drawing circles; optional--slides, cover slips, beaker with water, living organisms, dropper

> **Note:** *This is not intended as a beginning exercise in microscopy. Students must have some experience already with microscope use to gain the most from this lab.*

1. It is suggested to use prepared slides with static objects, or students can prepare their own slides with static objects.

2. Provide 250-400 mL beakers with which students can draw circles on their paper.

3. Remind students to label their drawings with a title, magnification (*not high or low power*), parts of an object as required by the teacher, and sizes of objects or parts of objects in µm.

4. Stress to students that microscrope drawings do not have to be 'Rembrandt Renditions,' but <u>do have to</u> <u>resemble</u> <u>and be proportional to</u> the object they are drawing. In this way they can 'measure' from their drawings.

5. **Indicate to students that an individual object viewed under low and high power should have nearly the same size estimates. Ex. Students will sometimes write that <u>the same paramecium</u> is 300 µm long when viewed under low power and 100 µm when viewed under high power!**

Copyright Spectrum Publications All Rights Reserved

Extensions:

1. During every microscope lab after this one, have students estimate the size of the organisms or objects they are looking at.

2. More experienced students might like to estimate the size of moving organisms such as paramecia or euglena. Use methyl cellulose to slow the movement of fast protists.

Answers to Questions:

1. micrometer = μm

2. μm

3. 1000μm = 1 mm

4. a. .5mm   b. .23 mm   c. 1300 μm   d. 620 μm

5. Approximate sizes of organisms/cells in μm: a. 700μm   b. 175 μm   c. 60 μm
   d. Length = 50μm   width = 25 μm.

Laboratory- Determining the Size of Objects under the Microscope

6 - 7. √

8. Although it varies with the different brands of microscopes,100X will typically range from 1.3-1.5 mm across the field of view.

9. 1.3- 1.5 mm = 1300- 1500 μm.

10. Student calculations.

11. Student drawings.

12. Student size estimations.

13. The field of view decreases as the magnification increases.

14. The size estimates for the same object viewed under low and high power will necessarily have to be very close to the same.

Surface Area to Volume Ratio *Teacher Background*

Purpose:
Students will calculate surface area: volume ratios and realize their importance for living things.

Objectives:
After completing this activity, students will be able to:

1. Discuss the importance of diffusion for living things.
2. Relate surface area : volume ratios to diffusion.
3. Calculate surface area : volume ratios for 'cells' of various sizes.

Time:
Prelab- 30 minutes   Laboratory- 50 minutes

Math Preparation:
1. Discuss how surface area is calculated and that it is measured in square units. Discuss how volume is calculated and that it is measured in cubic units.
2. Have students practice going from circumference to diameter to radius.

Laboratory Preparation and Tips:
Materials: Plastic baggie (cell), string, ruler, 100 mL graduated cylinder, water, calculator

1. Balloons are not used because water cannot be simply poured into them. Plastic baggies are used instead.
2. Make sure students measure around the widest circumference of the baggie each time another 100 mL's is added.

Extensions:
Students can make cubic 'cells' out of cardboard and calculate SA/V ratios for them.

Answers to Questions:
1. Diffusion is the movement of a substance from an area of higher to lower concentration.

2. Diffusion is used by the cell to bring in needed substances and eliminate wastes.

3. The digestive and respiratory systems depend on diffusion.

4. The surface area/volume ratio of a large cell would not allow the fast enough movement of substances to sustain the cell.

5. The surface area to volume ratio must be maintained. This can only happen with small cells. For an organism to grow larger, it must produce more small cells. For still larger organisms, circulatory systems provide oxygen and nutrients to cells.

9   *Copyright Spectrum Publications   All Rights Reserved*

6. The cell in example 1 would have more diffusion because of a higher SA/V ratio. The higher the SA/V ratio, the better for the cell.

7. A cell needs a high SA/V ratio to allow sufficient nutrients in and wastes out.

8. a. Volume $= 2$ cm x 3 cm x 4 cm $= 24$ cm^3
      S. A. $=$ (4cm x 2cm x 2 sides) $+$ (4cm x 3cm x 2 sides) $+$ (2cm x 3cm x 2 sides) $= 52$ cm^2

$$SA/V \text{ ratio } = 52 \ / \ 24 \ = \ 2.17$$

   b. Volume $= 6$ μm x 8 μm 10 μm $= 480$ μm^3
   S. A. $=$ (6 μm x 10μm x 2 sides) $+$ (6μm x 8μm x 2 sides) $+$ (8μm x 10μm x 2 sides) $= 376$μm^2
$$SA/V \text{ ratio } = 376 \ / \ 480 = .78$$

9. a. radius $= 4$ cm   Volume $= 4/3 \ (3.14) \ (4)^3$ V$= 267.9$ cm^3
                     Surface area $= \ 4 \ (3.14) \ (4)^2 \ = 201$
                     SA/ V ratio $= \ 201 \ / 267.9 \ = \ .75$

   b.   diameter $= 1.5$ mm   radius $=$ diameter/2 $= \ 1.5/2 = .75$
                     Volume $= 4/3 \ (3.14) \ (.75)^3 \ = 1.76$
                     Surface Area $= 4 \ (3.14) \ (.75)^2 \ = 7.065$
                     SA/V ratio $= \ 7.065/1.76 = \ 4.01$

10. 8a has a better SA/V ratio than 8b.   9b has a better SA/V ratio than 9a.   The higher the ratio, the better off the cell is.   Rank order from best --> worst $=$ 9b-->8a-->8b-->9a.

11. Hypothesis$=$ As the baggie is filled with more water, the SA/V ratio will decrease.

Laboratory-- Surface Area/Volume Ratio in a Growing 'Cell'

12. - 17. $= \sqrt{}$

18. The cell with the least volume and most surface area, typically the baggie with 100 mL's of water.

19.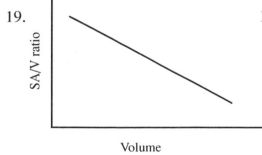

19a. As the volume increases, the SA/V ratio decreases, as shown by this graph. At a certain point the diffusion of materials will not sustain the cell.

20. Cells are small to maintain a high SA/V ratio so that diffusion of materials across the cell's membrane can support the cell's metabolism.

Diffusion in Potatoes

Purpose:

Students will learn how osmosis and diffusion work using potato cells.

Objectives:

After completing this laboratory, students will be able to:

1. Diagram and describe hypertonic, hypotonic and isotonic environments.
2. Calculate the volume of a cylinder.
3. Describe what happens to a potato core in hypertonic, hypotonic, and isotonic solutions.
4. Determine the sugar concentration which is isotonic to potato cells.

Time:

Prelab - 30 minutes   Laboratory, day 1- 50 minutes   Laboratory, day 2 - 50 minutes

Math Preparation:

1. Explain how to find the volume of a cylinder.
2. The graph which results from this laboratory uses negative values, which may give students some problems. Explain how to set up this kind of graph and interpret it.

Laboratory Preparation and Tips:

Materials: White potato, razor blade, metric ruler, balance, labels, paper towels, graduated cylinder, dissecting needle, aluminum foil or plastic wrap, large test tubes, distilled water, 10% and 20% sugar water, cork borers.

1. 10% sugar water (by volume) - (100 mL) Measure 10 mL of sucrose and pour it into a 100 mL graduated cylinder. Add water until 100 mL's is reached.

2. 20% sugar water (by volume) - (100 mL) Measure 20 mL of sucrose and pour it into a 100 mL beaker. Add water until 100 mL's is reached. Gentle heating or rapid shaking may be necessary to get the sugar into solution.

3. Each group will need 10 mL's of 10% and 20% sugar. Make the appropriate amount of each sugar.

Safety: Instruct students how to use razor blades properly.

Extensions:

1. Students can try the same experiment with apples, pears, etc. They can also use different types of sugars such as glucose, fructose, etc.

Answers to Questions:

1. Diffusion is the movement of a substance from an area of higher concentration to an area of lower concentration. No energy is used.

2. Hypertonic solutions contain more dissolved solute compared to another solution. Hypotonic solutions contain less dissolved solute compared to another solution. Isotonic solutions contain an equal amount of dissolved solute.

3. A solvent is a substance which can dissolve a solute. A solute is a dissolved solid.

4. Osmosis is the movement of water across a membrane from an area of high concentration to an area of low concentration.

5   a. The solution outside is hypotonic to the solution in the bag. Sugar will leave the bag into the beaker. The concentration of water is higher in the beaker than inside the bag, so water will flow into the bag. Since there is more water than sugar, the bag will swell in size.

     b. The solution outside is hypertonic to the solution in the bag. Sugar will go from the beaker into the bag. The concentration of water is higher inside the bag than in the beaker. It will leave the bag into the beaker, causing the bag to shrink.

6. Student hypotheses concerning the length, mass, and volume of the potato cores before and after the experiment.

Laboratory- Diffusion in Potatoes

7. - 17. = √

18. Typically, all the graphs should show a straight line with a negative slope.   18a. This number should indicate where the graph line crosses the X axis of the mass graph. This is the sugar concentration which is isotonic to the potato cells. Graphs shown below are approximate.

a. 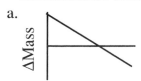   b. 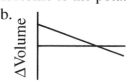   c.

19. As the percentage of sugar water increases, the length, mass, and volume of the potato core decrease.

20. a) At 0% sugar, the amount of water in the solution is 100%. It will tend to flow into the potato cores which will have less than 100% water. The potato cores will expand in size.

   b) At 10% sugar and 90% water, there is more water in the potato cores than in the solution, so the water will flow out of the potato cores into the solution. The potato cores will shrink.

   c) At 20% sugar and 80% water, there is considerably more water in the potato cores than the solution, so much water will flow out of the potato cores into the solution. The potato cores will shrink considerably.

Enzymes and the Rate of Reaction *Teacher Background*

Purpose:
Students will understand what an enzyme is, how it works, and how its rate of reaction is determined.

Objectives:
After completing this lab, students will be able to:

1. Describe the action of an enzyme.
2. Write the equation describing the catalase-hydrogen peroxide reaction.
3. Calculate the rate of reaction of an enzyme.

Time:
Prelab- 50 minutes   Laboratory- 50 minutes

Math Preparation:
1. Review with students what a rate is.
2. Make sure students have correctly calculated the rate of reaction in Problem #5.

Lab Preparation and Tips:
<u>Materials:</u> *Per group of 4 students:* 30 mLs of fresh 3% hydrogen peroxide, 30 mLs of liver water mixture, 100 mL graduated cylinder, 10 mL graduated cylinder, 250 mL Erlenmeyer flask, glass tube in rubber stopper which fits the Erlenmeyer flask, 40 cm long rubber tubing which fits the glass tube, water tub, stop watch, **goggles**

Note: Why is this lab called a simulation?? The technique used in this lab is a simple, inexpensive method to simulate the results of enzyme rate reactions requiring much more complex equipment.
  1) The curve is actually generated when students pour the liver water mixture into the hydrogen peroxide. As the liver mixture spreads through the hydrogen peroxide, the reaction occurs.
  2) The steepness of the curve will mostly depend on how fast the students can pour their mixture and cap the flask, not on the actual reaction rate of hydrogen peroxide and catalase.
  3) Pure enzyme is not being used.

Despite these factors, the simulated curves which students generate from this lab look very similar to the real thing and allow for easy rate analysis and calculations.

<u>Preparing the Liver Solution</u>
1. You will need 30 mL's of 3:1 water-liver mixture for each group doing the lab.
   a. For each gram of liver add 3 mL's of water. Use the blender on high until a smooth homogenate is produced.
2. Make extra water-liver mixture since it may take 4-5 trials to get three trials that are satisfactory. Some practice trials may be necessary for students to feel comfortable with the procedure.

3. Use fresh 3% Hydrogen Peroxide.
4. The amount of liver water and hydrogen peroxide (10mL's each) has been selected so that each trial is completely done in one minute.

In General
1. Have students practice filling the graduated cylinder so that it contains no air bubbles.
2. Occasionally when students add the liver mixture to the hydrogen peroxide, a 'blowout' will occur. This means all of the oxygen is produced very quickly and no results are obtained. Have students pour the liver water mixture into the flask somewhat more slowly.

Extensions:

1. Using a syringe and a two hole stopper, you can increase the accuracy of the measurements. Drill out the part of the syringe where the needle is normally inserted. Connect the rubber tubing to the glass tubing coming out of one hole, and insert the syringe with the liver water into the other hole. To prevent a 'blowout,' inject the liver water slowly, taking 3-4 seconds.
2. Add .1M HCl or NaOH to the liver water mixture, then try the experiment to see what effect acid and base have on the rate of reaction of the enzyme.
3. Boil or freeze the liver water mixture, then try the experiment to see what effect temperature has on an enzyme.

Answers to Questions:

1. Enzymes are large protein molecules which speed up chemical reactions by lowering the energy of activation of the reacting molecules.
2. Catalase is an enzyme which removes toxic hydrogen peroxide out of cells. The substrate for catalase is hydrogen peroxide.

$$H_2O_2 \xrightarrow{\text{Catalase}} H_2O + O_2\uparrow$$

3. A rate is the speed at which something occurs during a certain time period. The rate is calculated as: $\dfrac{y_2 - y_1}{x_2 - x_1}$

4a. Rate for seconds 0-20 = $\dfrac{42 - 0}{20 - 0}$ = $\dfrac{42}{20}$ = 2.1 mL's of O_2 / sec

   b. Rate for seconds 20-40 = .55 mL's of O_2 / sec   c. Rate for seconds 40-60 = 0 mL's of O_2 / sec
5. Seconds 0-10 = fast; 10-20 = medium;   20-30 = medium; 30-40 = slow; 40-60 = ~0

Laboratory- A Simulation: The Reaction Rate of Catalase and Hydrogen Peroxide

6. - 15.= √

16. See Graph. ----->
17. Seconds 0-10 = fastest rate; Seconds 10-20 = medium rate; Seconds 20-30 = medium; 30-40 = slow; 40-60 = ~0
18. Initially there is a large amount of substrate for the enzyme to work on, so the angle of the curve is steep and rate is fast. As more and more of the the hydrogen peroxide is converted into water and oxygen, the rate will slow down and the curve will flatten out.

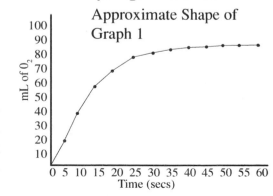

Approximate Shape of Graph 1

^{14}C Age Determination

Purpose:

The purpose of this activity is to have students work with a ^{14}C graph to determine the age of various organic fossils.

Objectives:

After completing this lab, students will be able to:

1. Describe how radioactivity is produced.
2. Explain why ^{14}C is used to date old organic material.
3. Discuss the half-life of a radioactive substance.
4. Graph the half-life of ^{14}C.
5. Determine by interpolation the age of organic material from the graph.

Time:

Introduction- 25 minutes   Activity- 35 minutes

Math Preparation:

1. Discuss the concept of the half-life of a radioactive substance and why this number is important.
2. Demonstrate how to interpolate using a graph.

Activity Preparation and Tips:

<u>Materials:</u> Pencil or pen, ruler

1. Discuss the limitations of the ^{14}C dating technique, i.e., it can not be used on material older than about 60,000 years. In addition, calculating the actual amount of ^{14}C remaining in an old organic specimen is subject to debate, as well.

Extensions:

1. Have students do a report on Carbon 14 dating. Have them search for famous artifacts such as the Shroud of Turin which were dated with this method.

Answers to Questions:

1. When the number of protons changes, a new element is created. When the number of electrons changes, an ion is created. An isotope is produced when the number of neutrons changes.
2. Radiation is produced when the number of neutrons in the nucleus of an atom makes the atom unstable, and alpha particles (He nucleus), beta particles (electrons), or gamma rays are emitted from the atom.
3. The half life of a radioactive substance is the amount of time it takes for half of a given amount of that substance to change into more stable elements.
4. ^{14}C is a radioactive isotope of Carbon. It is produced when cosmic rays interact with the atmosphere. Its half life is 5730 years.
5. The ^{14}C to ^{12}C ratio of an old organic object is compared with a similar living one.
6. No, it cannot. A dinosaur fossil is 1) too old, and 2) is a stone remnant of what was once a bone.

Activity- Determining the Age of Old Organic Objects

7.

Table 1

¹⁴C to ¹²C Ratio	Half Lives	Years
1.0	0	0
.5	1	5,730
.25	2	11,460
.125	3	17,190
.063	4	22,920
.0313	5	28,650
.016	6	34,380

8.

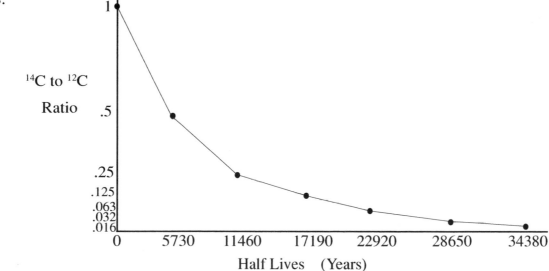

9. Answers are approximations:

¹⁴C/ ¹²C Remaining	Age (Years)
.06	22,920
.30	10,000
.57	5,000
.89	1,200

10. The shape of the Carbon 14 graph is a curve. Every additional half-life sample contains half of the preceding amount of Carbon 14.

11. This method gives accurate ages of old organic objects up to about 60,000 years. It can only be used with organic objects and it is not useable beyond about 60,000 years.

Pigment Chromatography

Purpose:

Students will learn through experimentation that 'green' tissue in a leaf is made up of several light absorbing pigments which can be separated by chromatography.

Objectives:

After completing this laboratory, students will be able to:

1. Diagram and describe the electromagnetic spectrum.
2. Describe the constituents of white light.
3. Explain how chromatography works.
4. Calculate R_f values for various chlorophylls.

Time:

Prelab - 20 Minutes   Laboratory- 50 minutes

Math Preparation:

1. Explain what an R_f value is, how it is calculated using the example, and what R_f values are used for.

Laboratory Preparation and Tips:

<u>Materials:</u> Large test tube, fitted rubber stopper, pin or paper clip, chromatography solvent, ruler, chromatography paper roll, spinach leaf, paper towel, 10p finishing nail.

1. The chromatography solvent consists of 90% Petroleum Ether and 10% acetone.

   Safety! Make sure students handle the solvent carefully. They should recap the solvent source bottle immediately after use, put their sample into the test tube quickly, and stopper it tightly. Have students work under a hood if one is available. If not, all doors and windows should be open, or work outside. Any open flames must be extinguished!!

2. The spinach leaves need to be fresh.
3. *Make sure students measure the solvent front first after removing the chromatography strip. The solvent front will evaporate quickly!!*

Extensions:

1. Have students try other types of plants to see what type of chlorophyll bands they get.

Answers to Questions:

1. Visible light.

2. Student drawing.

3. Pigments are molecules which can absorb discrete wavelengths of light.

4. No, pigments absorb different wavelengths than those they reflect. Example= chlorophyll, which reflects green, but absorbs blue and red.

5. Red and blue.

6. 7 / 10.6= .66   8 / 10.6= .75   9.8 /10.6 = .92

7. Chromatography works by separating out pigments of differing solubility in the solvent.

Laboratory- Separation of Photosynthetic Pigments using Chromatography
8. - 18.= √

19. Typically, students will be able to see 4 bands - 2 yellow and 2 green.   Plants have different pigments to absorb different wavelengths of light.

20. Each band is a pigment.

21. Pigments can be separated based on their different solubilities.

22. Actual bands => R_f carotene= .95 - .99 (a faint yellow line)

R_f xanthophyll= .4 (yellow)

R_f chlorophyll a= .2 (bright green)

R_f chlorophyll b = .1 (green- yellow line)

Measuring pH in Zygocactus   *Teacher Background*

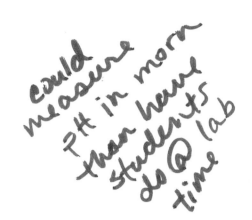

Purpose:

• Students will learn about pH changes in a living thing.

Objectives:

• After completing this lab, students will be able to:

  1. Explain what pH is.
  2. Calculate a pH.
  3. Calculate logs and antilogs.
  4. Measure pH fluctuations in Zygocactus.

Time:

Prelab- 30 minutes   Laboratory- First day: 30 minutes per class; thereafter- 10 minutes per day.

Math Preparation:

1. It is useful to review powers of 10—both positive and negative— before beginning the Prelab. Remind students that negative logs represent numbers between 0 and 1, and 10^{-3} is larger than 10^{-5}, for example. Any scientific calculator will have logs and antilogs.

Laboratory Preparation and Tips:

Materials: Per class- One *Zygocactus* with at least 50 leaves. Per Group- clamp, pH meter, 2 standardized buffers at different pH, deionized water, one 50-mL beaker, mortar and pestle, cheesecloth.

1. Zygocacti are inexpensive and easily obtainable at local nurseries and discount stores such as K-Mart and Target, especially around Christmas time, hence their other name, the Christmas Cactus.
2. Zygocacti will show the most fluctuation in pH if exposed to outside conditions, ie. sunlight and outdoor temperatures. They are easy to maintain, requiring a minimum of water and care.
3. Care should be taken that the pH probe is calibrated properly and cleaned with distilled or deionized water between uses.

Extensions:

1. Using Acid Equivalents to Quantify the Data:
   This procedure takes into account the mass of the leaf. 1. After removing the leaf, find its mass in g. 2. Grind it in the mortar and pestle, then add 10 mL's of distilled water. 3. Strain the mixture through cheesecloth into a 50 mL beaker. 4. Insert a pH meter and record an initial reading. 5. Titrate the mixture with 0.01 M NaOH (or KOH) until a pH of 7 is reached. 6. The microequivalents of acid, which takes into account the mass of the leaf, can be determined with the following formula:

$$\frac{\text{mL of NaOH used in titration} \times 10}{\text{Mass of leaf in g}} = \text{microequivalents of acid}$$

2. Science Fair Ideas- Add different substances to the Zygocactus to affect the CAM and pH.

Answers to Questions:

1. 10^{-5}

2. 3.4

3. 11

4. $10^{-6.62}$

5. 1000

6. 1000

7. 10000

8. 10.6 - 8.2 = 2.4 antilog of 2.4 =   251.2; a base of pH 10.6 is 251.2 X stronger than a base of pH 8.2.

9. Zygocacti open their stomata at night to conserve water.

10. Carbon Dioxide

11. Calvin Cycle

Laboratory- Measuring pH in *Zygocactus*

12. - 16. √

17. The pH should be low during the morning and increase as the day continues.

18. low pH= morning   high pH = afternoon, evening   The pH is low in the morning because the acid has been building up all night as carbon dioxide is incorporated into organic acids.

19. Answers will vary.

20. Answers will vary. Method=   Highest pH - lowest pH = Difference. Take antilog of difference.

The Effectiveness of Antibiotics and Antiseptics *Teacher Background*

Purpose:
Students will learn how to measure the effectiveness of antibiotics and antiseptics against bacteria.

Objectives:
After completing this lab, students will be able to:

1. Use sterile technique when handling bacteria.
2. Explain the difference between an antibiotic and antiseptic.
3. Measure and analyze bacterial growth vs. various antibiotics and antiseptics

Time:
Prelab- 10 minutes; Laboratory Day 1 - 50 minutes; Laboratory Day 3- 50 minutes

Math Preparation:
1. Students must know how to measure in mm, to find averages, and to rank order results.

Lab Preparation and Tips:
<u>Materials:</u> Bunsen burner, Luria Broth powder, *E. coli* (See Lab Safety on page *ii*), Luria Broth Agar Base, wheel plating device, glass 'hockey stick', .1 mL pipette or pipetter with tips, alcohol, 3 antibiotics in disc form, 3 antiseptics, forceps, control discs, autoclave, antiseptic soap, petri dish

Two days before the lab is to be done--
1. Using filter paper, punch approximately 100 discs with a hand punch.

2. Prepare 100 mL of the Luria Broth according to instructions on the bottle. Pour 10 mL of the LB into 10 test tubes and cover with aluminum foil. Sterilize the test tubes for 20 minutes at 20 lbs. of pressure.

3. After the test tubes containing the LB have cooled, inoculate each with a sterile loop of bacteria.

4. Prepare Luria Broth Agar according to the instructions on the bottle. Sterilize the LB Agar for 20 minutes at 20 lbs. of pressure. Each petri dish plate should be poured with approximately 33 mL of sterilized agar, i.e., 1000 mL's of agar will make about 33 plates. Prepare 2 plates for each group. Wait approximately 20 minutes after the sterilized agar has come out of the autoclave before pouring the plates. Once you start to pour the plates, do not stop! Keep the flask sideways as much as possible to prevent contamination. The plates will be firmly gelled after 1 hour.

On the day of the lab--
5. Soak 25 disks in each of the antiseptics and 25 in distilled water (control).

6. Show students how to operate the antibiotic disc dispensers.

7. Demonstrate to students proper plating procedure:
   a) Dip hockey stick into alcohol.
   b) Immediately put the hockey stick into the Bunsen burner flame.
   c) Remove and let the flame go out.
   d) Place the plate to be spread on the wheel plating device.
   e) Open the plate slightly and insert the hockey stick. Move the wheel around in a circle and move the hockey stick across the agar gently to cool it down.
   f) Remove .1 mL of bacteria from the LB tubes.
   g) Squirt the bacteria into the center of plate and begin to move the wheel around in a circle.
   h) Move the hockey stick across it to spread the bacteria.

8. The bacteria should be grown at 37° C for 1-2 days.

Safety: Demonstrate or review with students how to behave around a Bunsen burner. Students with long hair must tie it back. Remind students not to open their plates after preparing them with bacteria and the antibiotic or antiseptic. Have students wash their hands with an antiseptic soap after the lab. After the bacteria have grown, and the rings of inhibition are apparent, there is no need to open the plates. Students can measure the rings of inhibition through the transparent plastic.

Extensions:
Different bacteria can be used.

Answers to Questions:
1. A pathogenic organism that causes disease.
2. Antibiotics are substances which kill or prevent the growth of bacteria in the body. They are produced by fungi and bacteria.
3. Antiseptics kill bacteria on surfaces.
4. The ring of inhibition is the clear area around an antibiotic or antiseptic disc where there is no bacterial growth.

Laboratory- The Effectiveness of Antibiotics and Antiseptics
5. - 15. = √
16.- 19. Answers will vary. Students will know by the size of the ring of inhibition.
20. The control is necessary as a comparison.
21. No, bacteria may respond differently to antibiotics in the body than they do on agar.
22. Different antibiotics affect different stages of the reproductive cycle of bacteria. *E. coli* may be more susceptible to some antibiotics than others.

Serial Dilutions

Purpose:
Students will learn about exponential growth, how to dilute a large population of organisms into countable numbers, and determine which sugar grows baker's yeast most effectively.

Objectives:
After completing this lab, students will be able to:

1. Describe exponential growth of a population.
2. Dilute a large population of cells into countable numbers.
3. Calculate the original concentration of the population.
4. Describe which sugar grows bakers's yeast most effectively.
5. Use sterile technique properly.

Time:
Prelab - 30 minutes   Laboratory- Day 1- 50 minutes   Day 3- 30 minutes

Math Preparation:
1. Go through the equation for exponential growth: $Y = a(C)^x$. Have students do several calculations so that they feel comfortable with the equation before doing the graph in 2a.
2. Review powers of 10--both negative and positive. Discuss how a dilution is done and why it is possible to dilute large populations and still know the concentration of the original population. Go through problems 4-5 on the Lab Data Sheet.

Laboratory Preparation and Tips:
Materials: Per group: 3 nutrient agar petri dishes (plates), 2 sterile dilution tubes with 9.0 mL sterile water, 1 sterile test tube, test tube rack, Bunsen Burner, glass spreader, alcohol, plating wheel, 1 mL pipettes and sterile tips or sterile plastic pipettes. For the class: 100 mL of 1% concentrations of the following sugars containing Baker's yeast: glucose, sucrose, fructose, maltose; 4 large test tubes, optional: vortex mixer.

1. On the day before the lab prepare the four sugar/yeast suspensions as follows:
    a. Make 100 mL of 1% sugar solutions of glucose, fructose, sucrose, and maltose.
        1) Add 1 g of a sugar to 99 mLs of distilled water.
    b. Pour 20 mL of the first sugar into each of 4 large test tubes.
    c. Repeat this for the remaining 3 sugars.
    d. Cover the test tubes with foil and sterilize at 20 lbs of pressure for 20 minutes.
    e. *On the day of the lab add .5 g of dehydrated baker's yeast to each tube and cover.*
2. Prepare 2 dilution tubes for each group doing the lab.
    a. Add 9.0 mL of distilled water to each small test tube.
    b. Cover the tops with aluminum foil.
    c. Sterilize at 20 lbs of pressure for 20 minutes.
3. Make sure the dilution tubes are mixed thoroughly each time with a vortex (circular) motion.
4. The agar plates must be incubated up side down.

5. Review sterile technique with your students.

6. Plating procedure:
   a. Dip the end of the glass 'hockey stick' into alcohol.
   b. Immediate insert this end into the flame of a Bunsen burner. Burn the alcohol off of the hockey stick.
   c. Place an agar petri dish on the plating wheel.
   d. Open the petri dish plate 1-2 cm and put the sterile end of the hockey stick inside.
   e. Move the plating wheel in a circular motion and simultaneously move the hockey stick back and forth across the agar to cool it down. The agar is delicate. Take care not to tear it.
   f. Get 1 mL (1000 µl) of sample in a pipette and squirt it onto the center of the agar.
   g. Once again move the plating wheel in a circular motion and simultaneously move the hockey stick back and forth across the agar. Stop after 5-6 back and forth motions.

Extensions:

Students can compare yeast numbers throughout the day. A graph of time vs. yeast number could then be made and compared to the graph exponential growth.

Answers to Questions:

1. The yeasts will go through exponential growth until food runs out and wastes build up.

2.

Gen.	Yeasts
1	2
2	4
3	8
4	16
5	32
6	64
7	128
8	256
9	512
10	1024

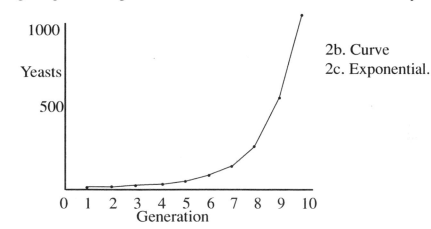

2b. Curve
2c. Exponential.

3. The yeast concentration is so high, it would produce an uncountable number on a petri dish.
4. 2.25×10^6 cells per mL.
5. He would dilute the cells by 10^{-2} to achieve 300 cells/mL to plate.

Laboratory- Which Type of Sugar grows Baker's Yeast most Effectively?

6. - 11. = √
12. Answers will vary.
13. - 14. =√
15. Bar Graph
16. Answers will vary.
17. Large populations are serially diluted by taking a small, known amount and mixing it with a large, known volume.

Fibonacci Sequences

Purpose:

Students will discover the Fibonacci Sequence and apply it to patterns in nature.

Objectives:

After completing this laboratory, students will be able to:

1. Calculate the Fibonacci Sequence.
2. Apply the Fibonacci Sequence to natural patterns found in pineapples, pinecones, and lettuce.

Time:

Introduction- 20 minutes   Activity- 30 minutes

Math Preparation:

1. Allow students to "discover" the Fibonacci sequence of numbers for themselves. They should be encouraged to explain the sequence in their own words.

Laboratory Preparation and Tips:

<u>Materials:</u> Pineapple, closed pinecone, artichoke, pencil or pen

1. Fibonacci numbers are found many places in nature-- 3 chambers in a bell pepper, a 5 point star cross section in an apple, and an 8 chambered cross section in a lemon. In sunflowers, the whorl of seeds is almost always a Fibonacci number. Pineapples, pinecones, and various types of lettuce are used in this laboratory because students will discover several Fibonacci numbers in the same fruit, vegetable, or pinecone which they can sequence.

2. Explain to students that care must be taken when counting the units or leaves on the steep, medium, and gradual inclinations on the pineapples and pinecones.

Extensions:

1. Have students bring in other fruits and vegetables and examine them for evidence of Fibonacci sequences.

Answers to Questions:

1. 13 pairs

2.

Month	No. of Rabbit Pairs
July	13
August	21
September	34
October	55
November	89
December	144

3. There will be 144 pairs of rabbits after one year.

4. a + b = next number in the Fibonacci sequence

Laboratory- Discovering Fibonacci Sequences in Nature

5. - 8. = √

9. Results will vary, but should represent Fibonacci numbers in the pineapples and pinecones. You can recognize Fibonacci numbers from the sequence.

10. Artichokes should also show Fibonacci numbers. You can recognize Fibonacci numbers from the sequence.

11. A Fibonacci sequence is a pattern of numbers which is calculated by adding two consecutive numbers in the sequence together to find the next number in the sequence.

   For any two consecutive integers in a Fibonacci sequence represented by a and b, the next integer in the sequence can be calculated as a +   b = next integer.

Percentage of O_2 in the Atmosphere

Purpose:

Students will learn how to determine the percentage of oxygen in the atmosphere using germinating pea seeds.

Objectives:

After completing this laboratory, students will be able to:

1. Describe oxygen and how it is used in respiration and regenerated in photosynthesis.
2. Explain why germinating pea seeds can be used to determine the percentage of oxygen in the atmosphere.
3. Calculate the percentage of oxygen in the atmosphere.

Time:

Prelab - 15 minutes   Laboratory: Day 1- 50 minutes   Day 2- 50 minutes

Math Preparation:

1. Explain to students how a percentage is calculated, and how it differs from a decimal number.
2. Explain how to calculate percentage error. Remind students about absolute values and why they are used to calculate the percentage error.

Laboratory Preparation and Tips:

Materials: Per Group—10 soaked pea seeds, 10 dry pea seeds, absorbant cotton, non-absorbant cotton, 15% KOH in a dropping bottle, thin test tube, 2 250 mL beakers, ruler, waterproof marking pen, ruler, **gloves, goggles**

1. Soak an appropriate number of pea seeds 1-2 days before the lab activity so that imbibtion occurs.

2. KOH is used to soak up any carbon dioxide in the test tube so that only oxygen consumption is measured. To make 15% KOH: Mass 15 grams of KOH, then pour it into a graduated cylinder. Add distilled water until the volume reaches 100 mL. **Caution!! KOH is a powerful base and must be handled with extreme care!!** Fill 1 dropping bottle per group with KOH.

3. Remind students to drip the KOH directly onto the cotton in the bottom of the test tube.

4. The wad of cotton holding the peas in place cannot be too thick, otherwise oxygen will not be absorbed by the peas.

5. Provide the percentage of oxygen in the atmosphere for question # 23 = 21%.

Answers to Questions:

1. Nitrogen and Oxygen.

2. An atom of oxygen has 8 protons, 8 neutrons, and 8 electrons. A molecule contains two atoms of oxygen. Atmospheric oxygen exists as O_2.

3. Plants and cyanobacteria produced it.

4. Respiration.

5. Photosynthesis$= 6\ CO_2 + 6\ H_2O \xrightarrow[\text{light and chloroplasts}]{} C_6H_{12}O_6 + 6\ O_2 \uparrow$

   Respiration $= C_6H_{12}O_6 + 6O_2 \longrightarrow 6\ CO_2 + 6H_2O + \text{Energy (ATP)}$

6. They are the reverse of each other. Oxygen, carbon dioxide, glucose, and water are used and regenerated.

7. No, they have no leaves and stems for photosynthesis, so they respire only.

8. Oxygen, because the seeds are using respiration to produce energy.

Laboratory- Determining the Percentage of Oxygen in the Atmosphere

9. - 19. = √

20. Approximately 21%

21. √

22. Answers will vary, but it should be approximately 21%.

23. Student calculations of percentage error.

24. Answers should be around 21%.

25. The class average should be around 21%.

26. The water level did not rise. The purpose of the control is to show that only respiring pea seeds are taking in oxygen.

27. Measurements were not accurate. Pea seeds did not use up all the oxygen. The KOH did not soak up all the carbon dioxide.

     28

The Ribbon of Life

Purpose:
Students will construct a timeline of life on earth and mathematically analyze it.

Objectives:
After completing this lab, students will be able to:

1. Construct a scale timeline of life on earth.
2. Research the appearance of new animals and plants and determine the dominant life forms in a time period.
3. Determine where to place life forms on the timeline based on their research.
4. Mathematically analyze the timeline to gain perspective about the history of life on earth.

Time:
Introduction- 10 minutes   Activity- 50 minutes x 2 days and student research time

Math Preparation:
1. Review ratios with students. They will need to use them when calculating the length of the timeline, periods in the timeline, and eras in the timeline.
2. Review percentages for the analysis questions.

Activity Preparation and Tips:
<u>Materials:</u>   String, butcher paper, coloring pencils or pens, tape, masking tape, scissors, yarn, glue (or glue sticks) drawing paper, textbook and/or reference books.

1. Obtain a roll of half-sized butcher paper. If this is not available or too costly, cut regular butcher paper down the middle to the desired length.

2. Be sure to have some reference books on hand so that students can research their time period. If your students have access to the Internet, use it to research the animals and plants.

Extensions:
1. Have students research more animals and plants for each period.

Answers to Questions:
1. The first organisms appeared 3.5 billion years ago. They were similar to the archaebacteria of today.

2. 30 million years elapsed between metazoans and vertebrates.

3. Between 570 and 550 million years ago almost all modern phyla appeared.

4. At least five major extinctions have taken place in the last 570 million years. The extinction which wiped out the dinosaurs at the K-T boundary is only one of the major extinctions, but the best known.

Activity- A Mathematical Ribbon of Life

5. 100 million years = .5m $\dfrac{.5m}{.1\ \text{billion}} = \dfrac{X}{4.5\ \text{billion}}$ 4.5 billion (.5m)= .1 billion (X)

                      2.25 billion m = .1 billion (X)   X= 22.5 m

6. $\dfrac{3.9\ \text{billion}}{4.5\ \text{billion}} = \dfrac{X}{22.5m}$ X= 19.5 m of string

7.   600 million years = 3 m of butcher paper.

8. - 15.   = $\sqrt{}$

Note: Depending on your references, the answers may vary somewhat.
Reference for these answers: Campbell, Neil *Biology* Third Edition, 1993

16.   1.1/ 4.6 = 24% of the earth's history there was no life. 76% of the time with life.

17. 4.6---> 3.5 billion years = 1.1 billion years; 4.6---> 2.5 billion years= 2.1 billion years. Early photosynthetic organisms had to produce oxygen.

18.   3.5 billion years ---> 1.5 billion years = 2 billion years

19.   1.5 billion years---> .6 billion years= 900 million years

20. a. ~550 million years ago. b. ~500 million years ago. c. ~350 million years ago.   d. ~300 million years ago. e. ~200 million years ago (There is still much controversy concerning the origin of birds. Any date is speculative.)   f. ~300 million years ago. g. ~120 million years ago.

21. Dinosaurs ruled the earth for ~183 million years, from the beginning of the Triassic (248 million years ago) to the end of the Cretaceous (65 million years ago).
                Percentage = 183,000,000 / 4,500,000,000 = 4%

20. Once again the date of the appearance of modern humans is fraught with controversy, but *Homo sapiens* skeletons anatomically like modern human beings have been found which are 100,000 years old.   100,000 / 4.5 billion = .00002= .002%

Stimuli, Senses, Time of Response   *Teacher Background*

Purpose:
Students will use gravity to help time how fast senses respond to different stimuli.

Objectives:
After completing this laboratory, students will be able to:

1. Calculate the time an object has fallen due to gravity.
2. Determine which stimulus—light, sound, or touch—produces the fastest response time.

Time:
Prelab- 30 minutes   Laboratory- 50 minutes

Math Preparation:
1. Review square roots with students—and how to find them on their calculators. Discuss what acceleration is and what the number 9.8 m / sec^2 means. Explain how it is possible to calculate time when only the distance is known by using the formula t= $\sqrt{2d/g}$.

Laboratory Preparation and Tips:
<u>Materials:</u> Meter stick, stack of paper towels, blindfold, calculator

1. Make sure students have something soft on the floor to cushion the meter stick should they miss it as it is falling. Students who are catching the meter sticks need to keep their fingers open the same distance each time to ensure unbiased results.

<u>Gravity</u>
Every object with mass will pull on every other object with mass. This force is called gravity. Although electrical and magnetic forces will both attract and repel, the force of gravity only attracts. When an object is released above the surface of a planet, it will fall towards the planet. As the object falls, it will gain speed, or accelerate. The acceleration of gravity is different for each planet. Here on Earth the acceleration constant for gravity is 9.8 m/sec^2. This means that for each second the object falls toward Earth, it will gain 9.8 m/sec of speed. Objects of any mass will accelerate at the same rate: An apple and a cannonball dropped at the same time will strike the surface at the same time. Just as the speed of an object can be calculated as it falls, the time of an object's fall can also be calculated. If the distance of a fall is known, using the acceleration of gravity constant it is possible to determine the time of the fall.

Extensions:
Response time under different circumstances can be tested, i.e. the respondant is listening to music, doing math, etc.

Answers to Questions:

1. Touch, sight, hearing

2. The body can react by secreting hormones or contracting muscles.

3. All electro-chemical impulses are the same.

4. Perception is achieved when different areas of the brain are stimulated. The number of neurons which fire determines the degree of stimulation.

5. $t = \sqrt{2d/g}$

6.

$$\sqrt{\frac{(2)\ 25\ cm}{9.8\ m\ sec^2}} = .23\ sec \qquad \sqrt{\frac{(2)\ .65\ m}{9.8\ m\ sec^2}} = .36\ sec \qquad \sqrt{\frac{(2)\ 212\ cm}{9.8\ m\ sec^2}} = .66\ sec$$

        a.   b.   c.

7. It is believed that response time will ... student predictions as to rank order of response times.

Laboratory- Which Stimulus Causes the Fastest Response Time?

8. - 20. $=\sqrt{}$

21. Student Graph

22. Typically, the sight response will be the fastest. Student explanations as to why the rank order came out that way.

Work, Power, and Calories

Purpose:

Students will calculate work, power, and calories after running up stairs.

Objectives:

After completing this laboratory, students will be able to:

      1. Calculate work, power, and Calories for exercise.

Time:

Prelab - 25 minutes   Laboratory- 30 minutes

Math Preparation:

1. Discuss the formulas for Work and Power and explain how work and power are different. Show how a Newton and a watt are derived.
2. Explain how joules can be converted into a measurement more familiar to students—the calorie. The difference between a calorie and a Calorie (kcal) should be emphasized.
3. The mathematics involved in calculating Work, Power, and Calories is relatively straightforward. However, since most students are not familiar with Newtons, Joules, or Watts, it will be necessary to go through the calculations sequentially.

Laboratory Preparation and Tips:

Materials: Stairway of at least 10 steps, meter stick, kilogram scale, stop watch, student volunteers

1. Make sure student volunteers are all in good health with no heart problems.
2. Make a table to record student name and watts of power on the board.

Extensions:

The Calories used during other types of exercise could also be monitored and calculated. Students could research the formula for horsepower, and calculate how many horsepower they produce in running up the stairs.

Answers to Questions:

1. Newtons; Joules

2. Watt

3. Work is the amount of force applied through a distance and is measured in Joules. Power is the amount of work done in a unit of time.

4. In biology and medicine, the calorie is used. For diet information, the Calorie (kcal), or 1000 calories is used.

5. A calorie is the heat energy necessary to raise 1 g of water from 14.5 to 15.5 °C. A kcal is 1000 calories. A Calorie (Kcal) is 1000 calories, the unit used in biological measurements.

6a.   W= Fd   Force = 63 kg x 9.8 = 617.4 N   617.4 N x 10 m = 6174 Joules
        6174 J/ 6.4 sec=   964.7 watts

6b.   W= Fd   Force = 42 kg x 9.8   = 411.6 N   411.6 N x 10 m= 4116 Joules
        4116J/ 5.3 sec = 776.6 watts

6c. Calories = Joules/ 4, 184   For problem 6a: 6174 J / 4,184 = 1.48 C
                                                          For problem 6b: 4116 J / 4,184= .98 C

Laboratory- Watts, Calories, and Running Up Stairs

7. - 14. = √

15. Typically, yes. The amount of watts will usually be well over 100.

16. Answers will vary depending on the mass of the persons running.

17. Force would have to decrease, or time must increase.

18. Time must increase.

19. Example: If a student has used .5 kcal to run the stairs—   .5 Cal (X) = 150 Calories

        150 / .5 = X   X= 300 secs, or 5 minutes to burn 150 calories

The Effect of UV Light on Yeast

Purpose:

The purpose of this lab is to introduce students to the effects of UV light on a test organism—the yeast.

Objectives:

After completing this lab, students will be able to:

1. Explain the effect of UV light on yeast growth.
2. Analyze colony growth on agar plates.
3. Describe where UV light fits into the overall Electromagnetic Spectrum.
4. Explain why UV light has a deleterious effect on yeast growth.
5. Demonstrate sterile technique for growing yeasts.
6. Calculate dilutions for yeast growth.
7. Accurately graph yeast growth vs. exposure time

Time:

Prelab - 20 minutes   Laboratory: Day 1 - 50 minutes   Day 2 - 50 minutes

Math Preparation:

Review dilutions and how titres are calculated.

Laboratory Preparation and Tips:

Materials: Per group: 2 UV sensitive liquid yeast cultures in petri dishes, UV lamp, **goggles**, 10 nutrient agar petri dishes, glass spreader, plating wheel, Bunsen burner or alcohol lamp, striker, 2 pipetters with sterile tips (or 10 sterile plastic pipettes), latex gloves, sterile cover dish, watch measuring in seconds.

Caution: Make sure your protective eyewear does not allow UV light to pass through. Students removing yeast must wear latex gloves. Use sterile technique throughout the lab. Insist that all students with hair 10cm or more in length tie it back around an open flame.

1. UV light sensitive yeast can be purchased from large scientific supply houses (Wards).
2. Making the nutrient agar plates: a) Make 10 nutrient agar plates per group   b) Mix nutrient agar with deionized water according to directions on the label of the nutrient agar jar. Sterilize at 20 lbs of pressure for 20 minutes.
3. Make sure students swirl or vortex mix the yeast suspensions and dilution tubes thoroughly each time.
4. Starting the yeast culture: Follow directions on package from supply house.
5. Use a germicidal UV lamp if possible. UV sensitive test cards are available from major scientific supply houses, as well. They can be used to test goggles before use.

6. "Plating" the yeast cells: a) Students dip glass spreader into alcohol and immediately place it into the Bunsen burner flame. Let the flame go out. b) Open the lid of the agar plate slightly and gently (the agar can tear!!) rub it across the agar 3-4 times to cool it down. c) Remove 100 µl (.1mL) from the second yeast dilution tube, carefully lift the cover of the agar plate just a crack, and inject the yeast onto the agar. d) Immediately turn the spreading dish wheel and move the glass spreader back and forth 5-6 times along it to spread the yeast evenly onto the nutrient agar. e) Close the plate cover.
7. Store the completed plates up side down at 37° C for 1-2 days in an incubator.
8. Make sure students do not open the petri dishes when counting the colonies.

Extensions:

1. Mix so-called antioxidant compounds in with the yeast to see if survivability is increased over a control.

2. Place UV filters (even sunglasses) above the yeast to test for the protective effects.

Answers to Questions:

1. Between X- Ray and visible light.

2. Approximately 15-400 nm.

3. More energetic, shorter wavelength.

4. 290-310 nm.

5. Damaged cells, aging, and cancer.

6. A small fraction.

7. UV light can damage the retina while causing no sensation of pain.

8. UV light kills germs .

Laboratory- The Effect of UV Light on Yeast

9. - 18. = √

19. Student data in graph.

20. The control is used to compare with the UV experimental yeast.

21. Analyzing the results: Theoretically, students will see a dose response to increasing time exposure to UV light. As the length of UV exposure time increases, fewer and fewer yeast cells will be observed because the UV light is killing them.

Purpose:

Students will learn how different children in a family receive different traits, using Mendelian genetics.

Objectives:

After completing this activity, the student will be able to:

1. Understand the possible combinations created with a crossing of 23 genetic traits.
2. Explain why brothers and sisters from the same family do not look exactly the same.
3. Calculate probabilities for different traits.

Time:

Introduction - 20 minutes   Activity- 45 minutes

Math Preparation:

1. Explain how to calculate probabilities from Punnett squares.

Activity Preparation and Tips:

<u>Materials:</u> two coins, pencil or pen

1. **The selected traits are not necessarily Mendelian nor do they reside on the chromosomes indicated. They are examples only.**

Extensions:

1. None

Answers to Questions:

1. It takes two alleles to make a trait.
2. The same chromosome from the mother and the father (eg. chromosome #1)
3. Three combinations are homozygous dominant, homozygous recessive, and heterozygous.
4. Taster could be PP or Pp and non-taster would be pp.
5. Both the mother and father contribute 23 chromosomes.
6. A normai human will have 23 pairs or 46 chromosomes.
7. Homozygous traits are the same so only one type may be contributed. Heterozygotes may contribute either one dominant or one recessive.

Activity- Human Traits and Probability

8. a. √   b. √   c. √

9. 1 of 4 offspring will have the recessive trait. 3/4 of the offspring will have the dominant trait ==Two will be heterozygous for the dominant trait and 1 will be homozygous dominant for that trait.

10. No, they will not be exactly the same. The probability that any two children will be exactly the same is extremely remote.

11. No, none of the children could get Retinitis Pigmentosa or Phenylketonuria. To get one of these recessive diseases, <u>both</u> of the parents would have to have the recessive allele.

12. 2^{23} = 8,388,608 to 1 that two children from the same parents will receive exactly the same chromosomes.

Crossing Over and Gene Mapping   *Teacher Background*

Purpose:
Students will learn how to use crossover frequencies to map genes to chromosomes in *Drosophila*.

Objectives:
After completing this lab, students will be able to:

      1. Use the results of linked gene crosses to calculate crossover frequencies.
      2. Use crossover frequencies to map *Drosophila* genes to chromosomes.

Time:
Introduction- 30 minutes   Activity- 50 minutes

Math Preparation:
1. Four basic math functions.

Activity Preparation and Tips:
<u>Materials:</u> Paper, pencil, calculator
1. Make sure students understand why this method only works with genes on the same chromosome, the so-called linked genes.

Extensions:
1. Students could compare this method of gene mapping to modern methods.

Answers to Questions:
1. 9:3:3:1

2. They explained the anomalous results by determining that the two genes they were studying were located on the same chromosome.

3. They explained the anomalous results for linked genes by determining that pieces of homologous chromosomes were breaking off and exchanging--crossing over.

4. See diagram on the bottom of the first page of the Crossing Over Activity. During a crossover event, identical pieces on homologous chromosomes break off and exchange position. The genes carried on those pieces produce new combinations of genes on the respective chromosomes.

5. Scientists realized that the frequency of crossovers between two genes on the same chromosome was directly proportional to the distance apart the two genes lay on the chromosome. The farther apart two genes are on a chromosome, the higher the crossing over frequency, and vice versa.

Activity- Mapping the Genes of *Drosophila*

6. X Chromosome

bar eye x *scalloped wings*   *white eye* x *scalloped wings*   *white eye* x *bar eye*

  c/o frequency= 3%   c/o frequency = 32%   c/o frequency = 35%

Chromsome 2

vestigial x *lobe eye*   *lobe eye* x *brown eye*   *vestigial* x *brown eye*

  c/o frequency = 6%   c/o frequency = 24%   c/o frequency = 30%

Chromosome 3

stubble x *spineless*   *stubble* x *ebony*   *spineless* x *ebony*

  c/o frequency= 1%   c/o frequency = 7%   c/o frequency= 6%

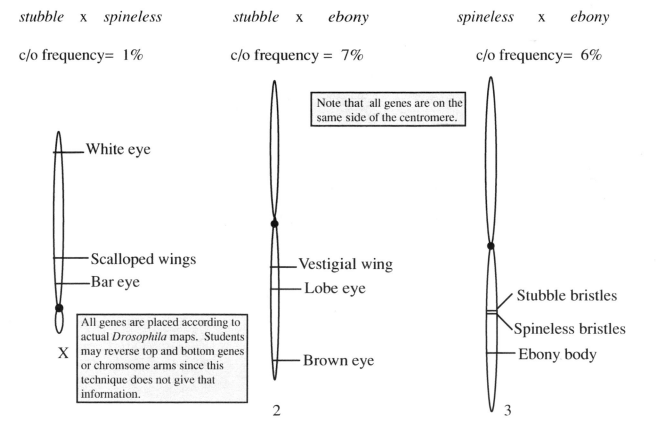

Note that all genes are on the same side of the centromere.

White eye

Scalloped wings
Bar eye

All genes are placed according to actual *Drosophila* maps. Students may reverse top and bottom genes or chromsome arms since this technique does not give that information.

X

Vestigial wing
Lobe eye

Brown eye

2

Stubble bristles
Spineless bristles
Ebony body

3

7. Researchers can place genes on chromsomes the correct distance apart. The exact positions of the genes on the chromosome cannot be determined from this technique.

8. No. Human beings produce too few children for the crossover frequencies to be established. It is unethical to experiment on human beings.

The Hardy-Weinberg Equation   *Teacher Background*

Purpose:
To introduce students to the Hardy Weinberg Equation and its use.

Objectives:
After completing this activity, students will be able to use the Hardy-Weinberg equation to:

    1. Determine the frequency of homozygous recessives in a population.
    2. Calculate the frequency of heterozygotes and homozygous dominants in a population.
    3. Determine the genetic health of a population.

Time:
Prelab- 40 minutes   Laboratory- 50 minutes

Math Preparation:
1. Show students how to find the frequency of students in their class who exhibit recessive traits. Explain that this number can be directly determined since a person showing a recessive trait as a phenotype must be homozygous recessive (genotype) for the trait.

2. Review finding square roots so that students can find q. Remind students to work sequentially through the equation as in the example, ie., they find q^2, then q, then p, then substitute these values into the equation. The Hardy-Weinberg equation is user friendly in that the values always will add up to 1, or very close to 1. If the values do not equal 1, students have made a mistake.

Laboratory Preparation and Tips:
<u>Materials:</u> Pencil, paper, calculator, PTC paper

1. The PTC paper should be relatively fresh. It will lose its taste after a long period of storage.
2. Have students put the PTC paper onto their tongues at the same time, and don't tell them what taste to expect. Their instantaneous reactions will signify who is a taster.

Extensions:
1. Students can use the Hardy-Weinberg equation to determine the frequencies of other traits besides those listed in the activity.

Answers to Questions:
1. The H-W equation is used to calculate the frequency of an allele in a population.

2. The genetic health of a population can be determined using the H-W equation.

3. The frequency of homozygous recessives must be known to use the H-W equation.

4. q^2 represents the homozygous recessive frequency. $2pq$ represents the heterozygous frequency. p^2 represents the homozygous dominant frequency.

5. The frequency of homozygous recessive traits can be directly calculated from the phenotypic frequency. q^2 can be directly calculated from observed frequencies counted in class.

6a. $p^2 + 2pq + q^2 = 1$ frequency of homozygous recessives = $1/3600 = .0003 = q^2$

$\sqrt{.0003} = .017 = q$ $p = 1 - q$ $.983 = p$

$(.983)^2 + 2(.983)(.017) + (.0003) = 1$; $.967 + .033 + .0003 = 1.0003$

Therefore, 96.7% (p^2) of persons of Jewish ancestry are free of the disease, 3.3% ($2pq$) are carriers, and 1 out of 3600 (.0003) (q^2) is affected.
Probability that 2 heterozygotes will meet = $.033 \times .033 = .0011 = 1$ in a 1000.
Probability heterozygotes will have a Tay-Sachs child = $1/2 \times 1/2 = 1/4$

6b. $p^2 + 2pq + q^2 = 1$ frequency of homozygous recessives = $1\% = .01 = q^2$

$\sqrt{.01} = .1 = q$ $p = 1 - q$ $.9 = p$

$(.9)^2 + 2(.9)(.1) + .01 = 1$

$.81 + .18 + .01 = 1$

81% of the Caucasian population is homozygous dominant for the CCR5 gene, meaning they are susceptible to the AIDS virus. Hardy-Weinberg predicts that 18% of the Caucasian population should be heterozygotes, but in fact 20% are. They are out of H-W equilibrium. The higher number of heterozygotes than expected in the actual population indicates that in the past, another virus perhaps used this receptor protein to enter human cells, then killed the host. Therefore there is a higher number of heterozygotes--who were better able to survive the initial attack--in the population today. This is a good example of natural selection.

Laboratory- Calculating Genetic Frequencies of Human Traits

7. Fill in Table 1.
8. Answers will vary.
9. Homozygous recessives are the only type where the genotype can be inferred from the phenotype.
10. If a trait is out of H-W equilibrium, it generally means that some selective pressures are at work in the population. Disease or a disaster affecting one phenotype over another could cause gene frequencies to change.

Probability in Biology *Teacher Background*

Purpose:
Students will determine what is to be expected of a certain outcome, what is probable, or what is likely to happen.

Objectives:
After completing this lab, students will be able to:

1. Determine the frequency of an event occurring using simple probability.

Time:
Prelab-1 hour   Laboratory -   1-2 hours

Math Preparation:
1. Review simple fractions, percents, and decimals with students.

Laboratory Preparation:
Materials: Coins, paper, pencil

1. Remind student that a Punnett square represents a hypothesis for an experiment.

Extensions:
1. Have students look into the probabilities of picking certain cards from a deck.
2. Have students come up with examples where probability can be applied to everyday life.

Answers to questions:

1. The determining of the frequency of an event or series of events.

2. A single event can be determined by dividing the event of choice by the number of possible events.

3. By multiplying the probability of the single events.

4. Rolling a 3 is 1 chance of 6 on one die. Rolling a 4 is also the same. So both would be 1 of 6 X 1 of 6 = 1 of 36. Rolling two 5s is 1 of 6 X 1 of 6 which = 1 of 36.

5. Flipping a head is 1 of 2 plus rolling a 3 is 1 of 6, so 1 of 2 X 1 of 6 = 1 of 12.

6. Having a daughter is 1 of 2, and each daughter would be 1 of 2, but to have one after the other would be 1/2 x 1/2 x 1/2 x 1/2 x 1/2 or 1/32.
The probability of have 4 sons would be 1/16.

7.a Normal pigmentation = N; Albinism=n

Nn x Nn

	N	n
N	NN	Nn
n	Nn	nn

3/4 = NN or Nn= normal skin

1/4 = nn or albinism

b. Round seed shape = R; wrinkled = r

Rr x rr (wrinkled)

	r	r
R	Rr	Rr
r	rr	rr

1/2 = Rr= Round

1/2= rr or wrinkled

c. Normal man = $X^N Y$; Carrier woman = $X^N X^n$

$X^N Y$ x $X^N X^n$

	X^N	X^n
X^N	$X^N X^N$	$X^N X^n$
Y	$X^N Y$	$X^n Y$

1/2 normal female
1/4 normal male
1/4 colorblind male

d. U = Unattached Earlobes; u = attached
Rh+= dominant ; Rh- = negative
Rh+Rh-Uu (male) x Rh-Rh-uu (fem.)
male gametes=Rh+ U; Rh+u; Rh-U; Rh-u
female gametes= Rh-u

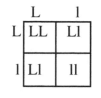

	Rh+ U	Rh+u	Rh-U	Rh-u
Rh-u	Rh+Rh-Uu	Rh+Rh-uu	Rh-Rh-Uu	Rh-Rh-uu

1/4 Rh+ Unattached; 1/4 Rh+ attached;
1/4 Rh- Unattached ; 1/4 Rh- attached.

Activities- Applying Probability in Biology

8. Typical hypothesis= 1/2 boys and 1/2 girls

9. - 13. √

14. Typically, the hypothesis will be more closely matched in the 'class' data because of a greater number of data samples.

15. L= long wings; l = vestigial wings

Ll x Ll

	L	l
L	LL	Ll
l	Ll	ll

Vestigial 1 of 4 or 25% (ll),
Long wing 3 of 4 or 75% (LL,LL)

16.-21 √

22. The hypotheis would typically bemore closely matched in the 'class' data because of a greater number of data samples.

23. The greater the sample size the more closely it will reflect the predicted (hypothesis) answers.

Analyzing Single Trait Crosses with χ^2 *Teacher Background*

Purpose:
To introduce students to chi square analysis of data.

Objectives:
After completing this lab, students will be able to:

1. Analyze an F_2 monohybrid corn cob.
2. Use a χ^2 statistical analysis to test the goodness of fit of the actual corn ratio and the predicted ratio (3:1).

Time:
Prelab- 50 minutes   Laboratory- 50 minutes

Math Preparation:
Chi Square calculations use simple mathematics to reach powerful conclusions. Go through the monohybrid example cross carefully with the students, then have them do the two practice problems on the Lab Data Sheet. Students must work in an organized, sequential manner making sure of their calculations along the way. A chi-square table is located in Appendix 1a of this book. One of the most difficult aspects of chi- square is using the χ^2 numbers in the table. They represent the probability that deviations from the expected occurred due to chance alone--a difficult concept for students. This needs to be discussed in detail with students.

Make sure students understand that a Punnett Square ratio represents a hypothesis--not what will happen, but what is predicted to happen. This predicted ratio can then be used to compare with actual data. The chi-square value allows a determination of the probability that the hypothetical ratio fits the actual data.

Laboratory Preparation and Tips:
<u>Materials:</u> Calculator, monohybrid F_2 corn, pins, paper, pencil

1. Stress the need to count and record the cob kernels accurately.

Extensions:
Corn cobs can also be ordered in 1:1 ratios. Try a 1:1 ratio cob.

Answers to Questions:

1a.

	N	N
n	Nn	Nn
n	Nn	Nn

F_1

	N	n
N	NN	Nn
n	Nn	nn

F_2 = 3 : 1

Normal wings: vestigial wings

437 + 138 = 575 total flies
575 x 3/4 = 431 = expected Normal wing
575 x 1/4 = 144 = expected vestigial wing

$$\chi^2 = \frac{(O_1 - e_1)^2}{e_1} + \frac{(O_2 - e_2)^2}{e_2}$$

$$\frac{(437 - 431)^2}{431} + \frac{(138 - 144)^2}{144} = .084 + .25 = .334 = \chi^2$$

Degrees of freedom $= 2 - 1 = 1$; .334 is found between .7 and .5 on the Probability Chart (Appendix 1a) This indicates there is a 50- 70% probability that deviations from the expected occurred due to chance alone. The data fit the hypothesis and the hypothesis can be accepted.

1b.   Pp   x   pp =

	p	p
P	Pp	Pp
p	pp	pp

1 : 1 ratio

227 + 202 = 429 total plants

429 x 1/2 = 214.5 expected purple flowered plants

429 x 1/2 = 214.5 expected white flowered plants

$$\chi^2 = \frac{(O_1 - e_1)^2}{e_1} + \frac{(O_2 - e_2)^2}{e_2}$$

$$\frac{(227 - 214.5)^2}{214.5} + \frac{(202 - 214.5)^2}{214.5} = .728 + .728 = 1.457 = \chi^2$$

Degrees of Freedom $= 2 -1 = 1$; 1.453 is found between .3 and .2 on the Probability Chart in Appendix 1a. This indicates there is only a 20- 30% probability that deviations from the expected are due to chance alone. The data do not fit the hypothesis well. An alternative hypothesis should be explored.

Laboratory- Analyzing Monohybrid Crosses with χ^2

2. The cross using symbols = PP x pp

3. √

4. √

5. √

6. √

	p	p
P	Pp	Pp
P	Pp	Pp

F1 = Pp

	P	p
P	PP	Pp
p	Pp	pp

F2 = PP, Pp= 3 Purple
      pp=   1 White

7. Using χ^2 on Group and Class Data

8. Answers will vary.

9. Answers will vary.

10. Typically, the class data will more closely conform to the predicted hypothesis because it will contain more samples. Sometimes, however, individual cobs may come very close to an exact predicted ratio.

Analyzing 2 Trait Crosses with χ^2

Purpose:

Students will learn how to analyze dihybrid corn crosses to see how closely they correspond to a 9:3:3:1 ratio.

Objectives:

After completing this laboratory activity, students will be able to:

1. Analyze an F_2 corn cob.
2. Use a χ^2 statistical analysis to test the goodness of fit of the actual corn ratio and the predicted 9:3:3:1 ratio.

Time:

Prelab- 50 minutes   Laboratory- 50 minutes

Math Preparation:

Chi Square calculations use simple mathematics to reach powerful conclusions. Go through the dihybrid example cross carefully with the students, then have them do the two practice problems on the Lab Data Sheet. Students must work in an organized, sequential manner making sure of their calculations along the way. A chi-square table is located in Appendix 1a of this book. One of the most difficult aspects of chi- square is using the numbers in the table. They represent the probability that deviations from the expected occurred due to chance alone--a difficult concept for students. This needs to be discussed in detail with students. Make sure students understand that a Punnett Square ratio represents a hypothesis--not what will happen, but what is predicted to happen. This predicted ratio can then be used to compare with actual data. The chi-square value allows a determination of the probability that the hypothetical ratio fits the actual data.

Laboratory Preparation and Tips:

<u>Materials:</u> Calculator, F_2 dihybrid corn cobs, pins, paper, pencil

1. Make sure students recognize the four phenotypic classes of corn seeds on the cobs and count them properly.
2. Write a table on the board for student groups to record their corn cob phenotype results.

Answers to Questions:

1a. Expected = 1:1:1:1 ratio   70 + 66 + 72 + 73 = 281   281 x 1/4 = 70.25

$$\chi^2 = \frac{(O_1 - e_1)^2}{e_1} + \frac{(O_2 - e_2)^2}{e_2} + \frac{(O_3 - e_3)^2}{e_3} + \frac{(O_4 - e_4)^2}{e_4}$$

$$\chi^2 = \frac{(70 - 70.25)^2}{70.25} + \frac{(66 - 70.25)^2}{70.25} + \frac{(72 - 70.25)^2}{70.25} + \frac{(73 - 70.25)^2}{70.25}$$

$$.41 = .00089 + .257 + .044 + .108$$

Degrees of Freedom = 4 - 1 = 3 : .41 at 3 degrees of freedom is found on the chi-square Probability Chart (Appendix 1a) between .90 and .99. This indicates there is a 90-99% probability that deviations from the expected were due to chance alone. The data fit the hypothesis extremely well.

1b. 152 + 62 + 47 + 19 = 280   Expected =   280 x 9/16 = 157.5 = striped, short = 9

280 x 3/16 = 52.5 = striped, long = 3

280 x 3/16 = 52.5 = green, short = 3

280 x 1/16 = 17.5 = striped, short = 1

$$\chi^2 = \frac{(152 - 157.5)^2}{157.5} + \frac{(62 - 52.5)^2}{52.5} + \frac{(47 - 52.5)^2}{52.5} + \frac{(19 - 17.5)^2}{17.5}$$

2.6 =   .129   +   1.72   +   .576   +   .192

Degrees of freedom= 4 - 1= 3 ; 2.6 at 3 degrees of freedom value falls between .5 and .3 on the chi-square Probability Chart, indicating there is only a 30-50% chance that deviations from the expected are due to chance alone. The data do not fit the 9:3:3:1 hypothesis well.

2. Cross using symbols = PPSS x ppss ; genotype of all F_1 offspring = PpSs; phenotype of all offspring = Purple, Smooth

PPSS x ppss =   ps   PpSs x PpSs = F_2

PS | PpSs |

F_2

	PS	Ps	pS	ps
PS	PPSS	PPSs	PpSS	PpSs
Ps	PPSs	PPss	PpSs	Ppss
pS	PpSS	PpSs	ppSS	ppSs
ps	PpSs	Ppss	ppSs	ppss

Purple Smooth=   9

Purple Wrinkled=   3

Non-Purple Smooth = 3

Non-Purple Wrinkled=1

Laboratory- Analyzing Dihybrid Crosses with χ^2

3.-7. √

8. Typically, students will be able to accept class data more readily than group data because of the larger sample size.

9. Typically, the class data will conform to the 9:3:3:1 ratio more closely than the group data because there is a larger sample size. Occasionally, there might be an individual corn cob which is almost exactly 9:3:3:1, but it is rare.

Building a Model of DNA

Purpose:
Students will build and use a large, working model of DNA.

Objectives:
After completing this activity, students will be able to:

1. Diagram and describe the structure of DNA, including: double helix structure, antiparallel structure, 3' and 5' ends, nucleotides, and A-T, G-C base pairing.
2. Discuss the function of DNA, including replication and transcription.
3. Calculate the dimensions of a scale model of DNA.

Time:
Prelab- 15 minutes. Laboratory--When students cut the matboards and glue the bases to sugars the first year= 1 hour. Thereafter, the time can vary at the discretion of the teacher as to how much of the model each period will build.

Math Preparation:
1. Students may need help setting up the ratio to calculate the length of the model.

Laboratory Preparation and Tips:
<u>Materials:</u> 2 m² of black matboard, 1 m² of white matboard, .5 m² of blue matboard, .5 m² of red matboard, .5 m² yellow matboard, .5 m² of green matboard, sharp scissors, razor blades, brass fasteners, Velcro with adhesive backing, glue; optional--> eyelet maker and eyelets

Used matboard can be purchased at some art or framing stores for a nominal amount. Depending on the time, either students or the teacher can trace the model parts onto the appropriate colored matboard. Each group should be assigned a specific length to build—usually 3-4 base pairs long. After each group is finished with its section, the sections should be put together. Each classes' sections can then be added together during the course of the day.

Sizes of DNA components: 1) Deoxyribose Sugar: A pentagon 6 cm on a side.
                                            2) Phosphate: 10 cm long, 2 cm wide, with a 2 cm wide crosspiece in the middle.
                                            3) Bases: 7 cm long, 3 cm wide.

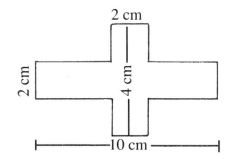
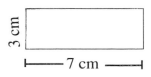

Suggestion: Use an Eyelet maker (available at yardage and sewing stores) to punch holes through the matboard at the places indicated. This will ensure that the model will not fall apart. One hundred brass eyelets typically cost between $1.00- $2.00.

After the initial year, the model can be disassembled and reassembled for years to come.

Extensions:

Since the bases are connected with Velcro™ it is easy to demonstrate replication by simply pulling the model apart down the middle, then adding nucleotides to the appropriate complementary bases. Similarly, transcription can be demonstrated by unzipping a part of the model down the middle to simulate a gene opening, then adding the appropriate RNA nucleotides. The action of restriction endonucleases can also be shown, as well as mutations.

Answers to Questions:

1. Watson and Crick

2. They built a model of DNA.

3. Watson and Crick based their model on diffraction X-Ray photographs taken by Rosalind Franklin.

4. DNA is 2 nm wide.

5. The repeat pattern of DNA is 3.4 nm.

6. Double Helix, antiparallel structure, 3' and 5' ends; A-T, G-C base pairings.

Activity- Building a Model of DNA

7.- 17.= √

18. Student drawing with characteristics of DNA.

19. $\quad \dfrac{2 \text{ nm}}{2 \text{ m}} = \dfrac{28 \text{ cm*}}{X} \qquad : \qquad \dfrac{2 \times 10^{-9} \text{ m}}{2 \text{m}} = \dfrac{.28 \text{m}}{X} \qquad =$

Convert to meters

$.56 \text{m} = 2 \times 10^{-9} \text{ m} \ (X) \qquad \dfrac{.56}{2 \times 10^{-9} \text{ m}} = X = 2.8 \times 10^{8} \text{ m}$

* Approximate width of model

Remind students to convert all labels in the formula to meters.

Restriction Analysis of Lambda DNA *Teacher Background*

Purpose:
The purpose of this lab is to determine the number of base pairs in restriction fragment bands.

Objectives:
After completing this laboratory, students will be able to:

1. Load and run a DNA sample through electrophoresis.
2. Aanalyze migration distances.
3. Construct a semilog graph of base pairs vs. migration distance
4. Use interpolation to determine the number of base pairs in unknown restriction fragment bands.

Time:
Prelab- 30 minutes   Laboratory-   100 minutes for loading and running the gel.
Typically, students will have to return sometime during the day to remove their gels for staining.
50 minutes for analysis.

Math Preparation:
1. Discuss what logs and antilogs are. Make sure students know how to find logs and antilogs on their calculators. This knowledge is necessary to construct and interpret the graph.

2. Discuss graph interpolations.

Laboratory Preparation and Tips:
Materials: Power supply, gel box, Phage lambda restriction digests using BstII E, HindIII and Eco RI; uncut DNA, 1% agarose, TBE running buffer, 10 µl pipettes and tips, loading dye, ruler, semilog graph paper, pencil, 1.5 mL microfuge tubes, microfuge, crushed ice, 400 mL beaker, permanent marker, gloves, scientific calculator, gel illuminator, camera, film, DNA stain

Many of the necessary chemicals /biologicals can be purchased in stock form or ready to use.
1. Already digested Phage Lambda DNA samples--BstE II, HindIII, and EcoRI--can be purchased from scientific supply houses--Wards or Carolina.
2. *If staining with methylene blue, increase the DNA per tube from 1µl to 5µl. Decrease water to 4µl.*
3. 1% agarose gels: 1 part agarose powder to 99 parts 1X TBE. Gels can be pre-cast or cast by students at the beginning of the lab.
4. TBE running buffer: can be purchased commercially in 50X or 20X stock solutions.
5. Loading dye: can be purchased commercially.
6. Make sure the DNA/restriction enzyme solutions are kept on ice at all times.
7. Film - Special high speed film must be used. It is Polaroid black and white #667, 3000 ASA.
8. **Safety! ——> Only a <u>teacher</u> trained in the safe and proper use <u>and</u> disposal of ethidium bromide should use it!! Refer to the MSDS on ethidium bromide!! Follow district guidelines if applicable. Follow company directions for proprietary DNA stains.**

Extensions:
More restriction enzymes beyond those used in the lab can be tried.

Answers to Questions:
1. Genes are found along the DNA.
2. A substance which cuts DNA at discrete sites.
3. A restriction enzyme cuts at a restriction site.
4. The DNA bands can be analyzed for size, sequence, mass, etc.
5. DNA is negatively charged due to the phosphates and will migrate from the – —> + poles on a gel.
6. The size of the band determines how far it will move. The smaller the piece of DNA, the farther it will move on a gel.
7. 19,388 base pairs.
8a. log of 2700 = 3.43   b. log of 878= 2.94   c. Antilog of 3.8 = 6310 d. Antilog of 2.1= 126

Laboratory- Restriction Analysis of Phage Lambda DNA

9. - 15. √

16. Actual number of base pairs for HindIII bands=
23,130;   9,416;   6,557;   4,361; 2,322;   2,027 **125**

Example Gel

Note: The bands with < 1 kbp may not be visible.

17.- 19. = √

20. **EcoRI** = 5 restriction sites = 6 pieces
21,226; 7,421; 5,804; 5,643; 4,878; 3,530

BstE II   = 13 restriction sites = 14 pieces
8,454; 7,242; 6,369; 5,686; 4,822;4,324; 3,675;
2,323; 1,929; 1,371; 1,264; **702; 224;117**

HindIII = 7 restriction sites = 8 pieces
23,130; 9,416;6,557; 4,361; 2,322; 2,027; **125**

21. Different restriction enzymes recognize different base sequences to cut.

22. The actual number of base pairs in Phage Lambda is approximately 48,500.

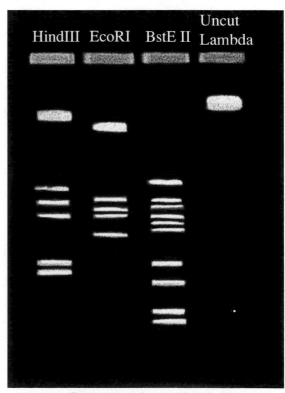

Computer enhanced for clarity

The Effect of UV Light on DNA   *Teacher Background*

Purpose:

The purpose of this laboratory is to determine quantitatively the effects of UV light damage on DNA.

Objectives:

After completing this laboratory students will be able to:

1. Discuss the three forms of DNA which result from UV damage.
2. Make, load, and run a gel with DNA.
3. Calculate the quantitative degree of DNA damage which results from exposure to UV light.

Time: Prelab- 50 minutes; Laboratory- Day 1= 50 minutes; Day 2 = 10 mins.; Day 4= 50 mins.

Math Preparation:

Students must know how to calculate square area and percentages.

Laboratory Preparation:

<u>Materials:</u> TBE (Tris-borate-EDTA) running buffer, gel box, agarose, power supply, pipette and tips, aluminum foil, DNA stain, loading dye, UV light, two 1.5 mL microfuge tubes containing plasmid DNA/ Deionized Water (D.I.) mixture, 12 1.5mL microfuge tubes, fine-tipped permanent marker, latex gloves, 2 trays containing ice, microfuge, gel illuminator, camera, film, ring stand, **goggles which block UV light.**

Background: Being able to quantify DNA strand breaks accurately in an isolated system is a fairly new technique. The quantification of these breaks can be achieved by using plasmid DNA, electrophoresis, and measuring the intensity of the bands produced. Ultraviolet (UV) light, located between visible light and X-rays on the electromagnetic spectrum, has been implicated in cell death and DNA damage, both of which are the subject of much research. The technique in this lab allows students to quantify DNA damage done by UV light. Although UV light is a part of the nonionizing region of the ES, it can still cause the production of free radicals. A free radical is produced when energy is transmitted to the electron shell which surrounds the nuclei of atoms or molecules, causing an electron to move to a higher energy level. Eventually, the electron will escape its atom or molecule, resulting in a free electron and an atom or molecule which is missing an electron. These electron-deficient free radicals are highly unstable and will react rapidly with the surrounding environment. One of the most important radicals is the hydroxyl radical (OH-) not only because it is one of the most reactive species, but due to its relative abundance as well. The hydroxyl radical is generated with irradiation through the hydrolysis of water. The OH- radical is commonly linked with genetic mutation, aging, and of considerable importance, DNA strand breakage. When a hydroxyl radical reacts with DNA, a strand break can occur. This happens because a hydrogen atom is abstracted off the base or deoxyribose sugar of the DNA, resulting in the breakage of the deoxyglycosyl linkage between base and sugar. As a consequence, breakage of the 3' sugar phosphate bond could occur. This breakage is particularly apparent in plasmid DNA since it is in the form of a circle. If only one strand break occurs on the supercoiled DNA, an open circle form will be generated. Similarly, if two strand breaks occur in close enough proximity, the DNA will assume a linear form. Each of these three forms--supercoiled, open circle, and linear--moves through an agarose gel at a different rate, allowing it to be identified. The band migrating the furthest will be supercoiled, followed by linear, and then open circle. See gel on next page.

Helpful Hints:

1. Setting up the 1.5 mL microfuge tubes: For ethidium bromide staining-- 45µl of D.I. water and 5µl of plasmid DNA, 2 tubes per group.   For methylene blue staining- 25 µl of D.I. water and 25µl of plasmid DNA, 2 tubes per group.
2. Agarose Gels: a) Make 1% agarose gels by mixing 1 part agarose to 99 parts   1X TBE solution. b) Make enough to cast the appropriate number of gels for your class.
3. TBE running buffer: a) can be purchased commercially in 50X or 20X stock solutions.
4. Plasmid DNA: pUC18 plasmid (or a substitute) can be purchased from commercial scientific supply houses.   **Make sure it is as near to 100% supercoiled as possible!! This will greatly enhance results!!!**
5. Loading Dye: Can be purchased from scientific supply houses.
6. Make sure the DNA is kept on ice at all times. Ice under the UV lamp will melt and will need constant resupply.
7. The National Institute of Health has a gel imaging program called **NIH Image** which is public domain and available online. It can be downloaded from: **http://rsb.info.nih.gov/nih-image** Look in the education area. This program is necessary to analyze the DNA bands quantitatively.
8. DNA staining--Some science supply houses have their own proprietary DNA stains, and there is always the standby- methylene blue. *Please see step 1. If you have been trained with ethidium bromide, your district allows its use, and you have camera equipment for it, it is much faster and more sensitive than the other DNA stains.*

Extensions:

Substances known to be free radical scavengers (i.e. vitamins) can be tested in this system.

Answers to Questions:

1. Nonionizing radiation 2. DNA breakage is apparent when using a plamid 3. Supercoiled 4. Open Circle 5. Linear 6. Student drawing should be similar to Diagram 2.

Laboratory- The Effect of UV Light on Plasmid DNA

7. -18. = √
19. Graph--

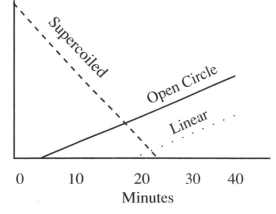

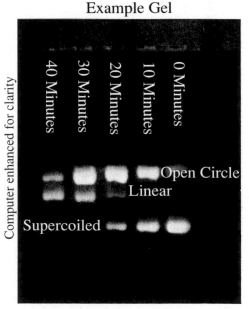

Example Gel

20. The percentage of supercoiled will decrease with increasing exposue to UV light, and the percentage of open circle and linear will increase as the DNA is damaged more and more.

Correlations

Purpose:

Students will learn how to use correlations to compare foot size vs. height in males and females.

Objectives:

After completing this lab, students will be able to:

1. Graph co-related data to determine if a linear relationship exists.
2. Use the correlation formula to determine the strength of a correlation.
3. Use the formula $r^2 100$ to determine the percentage of the total variation of the y's which is is accounted for by the relationship with x.

Time:

Prelab- 50 minutes   Laboratory- 50 minutes

Math Preparation:

1. The operant thought for this lab: **no fear** of large, imposing looking formulae. The formula for correlations is **easy to use** when broken down into parts. It contains addition, subtraction, multiplication, division, and square roots.

2. Remind students to be *very careful* when using the four functions and square roots. The math is not difficult, but there is a lot of it, and it needs to be done sequentially and *carefully*. Order of operation rules must be stricted adhered to.

3. Make sure students do the practice problem (#3) correctly.

Lab Preparation and Tips:

<u>Materials:</u> Meter stick, calculator, paper

1. Set up a Height and Foot Length Table on the board for males and females.
2. Students will probably need at least 2 separate pieces of paper for copying data and doing calculations.

Extensions:

1. There are many types of data which are co-related. Students can look at time spent studying vs. test scores or overall GPA vs. science GPA, etc.

Answers to Questions:

1. Student answers should resemble the three graphs found on the first page of the *Correlations* lab.
2. Mathematically, a correlation is described as being a linear relationship between two variables X and Y such that a change in X causes a predictable change in Y.

3.

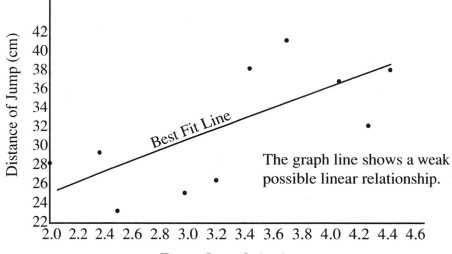

The graph line shows a weak possible linear relationship.

x	y	x2	y2	xy
4.3	32	18.49	1024	137.6
2.0	28	4.0	784	56
2.4	29	5.76	841	69.6
3.0	25	9.00	625	75
3.5	38	12.25	1444	133
2.5	23	6.25	529	57.5
3.2	26	10.24	676	83.2
3.8	41	14.44	1681	155.8
4.5	38	20.25	1444	171
4.1	37	16.81	1369	151.7
33.3	317	117.49	10,417	1,090.4

$$r = \frac{10\,(1090.4) - (33.3)(317)}{\sqrt{10\,(117.49) - (33.3)^2}\;\sqrt{10\,(10,417) - (317)^2}} = \frac{10,904 - 10556.1}{\sqrt{1174.9 - 1108.89}\;\sqrt{104,170 - 100,489}}$$

$$r = \frac{347.9}{(8.12)\;(60.67)} = \frac{347.9}{492.64} = .71$$

$r^2 100 = .50\,(100) = 50\%$

50% = a weak correlation

Laboratory - What is the Correlation of Foot Size to Height in Males and Females?

4. Student work

5. Student graph

6. Student correlations

Analysis

7. The closer the value for $r^2 100$ is to 1 or -1, the stronger the correlation.

The Central Tendencies of Data *Teacher Background*

Purpose:
Students will analyze the range, mean, median, and mode of student heights and graph the data.

Objectives:
After completing this lab, students will be able to:

    1. Find the range, mean, median, and mode of student heights.
    2. Graph the data.
    3. Interpret and analyze the range, mean, median, and mode of student heights.

Time:
Prelab - 50 minutes   Laboratory- 50 minutes

Math Preparation:
1. Explain to students that statistics does not involve complicated math, only an application of the math skills they already possess. A four function calculator can get them through range, mean, median, and mode.

2. Explain how to find the range, mean, median, and mode, then have students do Question 1 in the Prelab.

Laboratory Preparation and Tips:
Materials: Meter stick (or metric measuring tape), pencil or pen, graph paper

1. Copy Table 2 onto the board so that students can fill it out.

Extensions:
1. Students can add their data to those of other classes to find the range, mean, median, and mode for a larger sample size.

2. Students can be asked to hypothesize what would happen if natural selective pressures based on height were introduced into the human population, i.e., if persons above 180 cm in height could no longer produce viable offspring, what would eventually happen to the shape and position of the bell curve?

Answers to Questions:
1. Range = 2.05 - 1.55= .5 m   Mean = 57.72 / 32 = 1.80 m   Median = 1.83 m
   Mode = 1.83 m

Giraffe Neck Length Range (m)	# of Giraffes in this Range
1.5-1.59	3
1.6-1.69	4
1.7-1.79	7
1.8-1.89	11
1.9-1.99	5
2.0-2.09	2

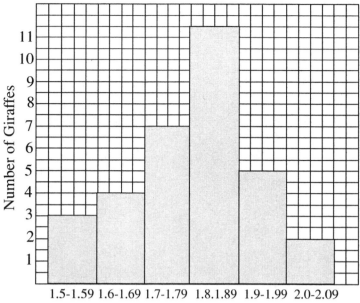

Laboratory- A Quantitative Analysis of Human Height

2. - 5. = Student measurements and calculations

6. The range gives the difference between the shortest and tallest person in the class.
   The mean gives the average height of all students in the class.
   The median is the value where half the class would be taller and half would be shorter.
   The mode is the most frequently occurring height in the class.

Analyzing a Normal Distribution

Purpose:
To analyze statistical measurements of a class' height.

Objectives:
After completing this lab, students will be able to:

1. Calculate variance, standard deviation, and a z score
2. Understand the idea of standard deviation
3. Use the z score to derive information about the class height.
4. Understand the idea of a normal distribution.

Time:
Prelab: 50 minutes   Laboratory: 50 minutes

Math Preparation:
1. Explain the concept of square roots and how to find it on a calculator. Have students do a few practice problems if necessary. Explain that the symbol Σ means 'sum of.'
2. Above all students need to know that statistics are not difficult. Using math skills many students already have—including square roots— they should be able to calculate the standard deviation and z score easily. The standard deviation is how far from the mean a sample is. Z scores are calculated to determine how many standard deviations from the mean a sample is. The z score can then be converted into an area corresponding to a frequency under the normal distribution line (bell-shaped curve). **See Appendix 1b for z scores.** Make sure students follow the examples step by step. Students must work in a sequential fashion.
3. Discuss with students that these statistics use a <u>sample</u> of a population to make an estimate about the <u>entire</u> population.

Laboratory Preparation and Tips:
<u>Materials:</u> Meter sticks, calculator, pen or pencil, paper

1. Draw a large data table on the board which looks like this:

$$Y - \overline{Y} \qquad \Big| \qquad (Y - \overline{Y})^2$$

Students write their heights in under the Y in the left column. $\overline{Y}$ is the mean and should be calculated after all the data are collected. In the right hand column, the difference is squared. The sum total of $(Y - \overline{Y})^2$ needs to calculated.

Extensions:
1. Students can statistically analyze any randomly distributed data set: hair length, weight, peas in a pod, etc.

Answers to Questions:

1.

a.

.5 m Interval	# of Trees
4.6 - 5.0	3
5.1 - 5.5	7
5.6 - 6.0	10
6.1 - 6.5	6
6.6 - 7.0	3
7.1 - 7.5	1

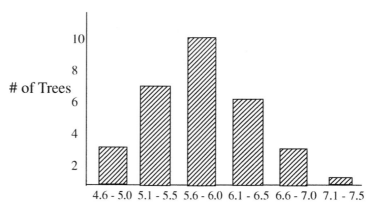

b. Mean = 5.8   Standard Deviation $= \sqrt{\dfrac{\sum (Y - \overline{Y})^2}{n - 1}}$ $\sqrt{\dfrac{11.23}{30 - 1}} = .62$

b1. % of population taller than 7.0 m=   z= $\dfrac{7.0 - 5.8}{.62}$ = 1.94   area on z chart = .4738

$$\begin{array}{r} .5000 \\ - .4738 \\ \hline .0262 \end{array}$$ **Based on the <u>sample</u>, 2.62% of the <u>population</u> is taller than 7.0 m.**

b2. % of population shorter than 6.5 m--> z= $\dfrac{6.5 - 5.8}{.62}$ = 1.13   area on z chart = .3708

$$\begin{array}{r} .5000 \\ + .3708 \\ \hline .8708 \end{array}$$ **Based on the <u>sample</u>, 87.08% of the <u>population</u> is shorter than 6.5 m.**

Laboratory- A Statistical Analysis of Height

2. Students make a table to record height data.

    2a. Students fill in Table 3 and make the histogram.

3. Students make columns for $Y - \overline{Y}$ and $(Y - \overline{Y})^2$.

    3a. Students find the mean and standard deviation for the class heights.

4. Student calculations.

    60

BEAIMs

Laboratories and Activities

Using the Metric System

Prelab

Throughout the world the metric system, or SI (System Internationale), is used as the standard system of measurement. The metric system was developed in France about 1790, and it replaced a system which was based on feet, pounds, inches, yards, and gallons.

The standard unit of length in the metric system is the **meter (m)**. It was originally based on 1/10,000,000 of the distance between the equator and the north pole. From the meter, volume and mass units were derived. The **liter (l)**, the standard measurement of volume in the SI, is calculated from one decimeter cubed (dm^3.) The mass of a liter of water at standard temperature and pressure is called the **kilogram (kg)**—the unit of mass in the SI.

A dm^3 (liter) of water has a mass of 1 kg.

Advantages of the Metric System
1. Since each SI unit can be derived from another, there is great flexibility in the metric system.
2. The SI is a decimal system, so basic units can be subdivided by 10 or increased by multiples of 10.
3. Latin prefixes are used to denote the part of the basic unit used, or how many of the basic unit were used. Units in the metric system are abbreviated by using the first letter of the Latin prefix and the first letter of the basic unit— Kilometer= km ; millimeter = mm; the exception-- dekameter = dkm

Changing Units in the SI
Often it is necessary to change units in the Metric System for use in formulas or for convenience. To change units in the SI, become familiar with this chart:

1000	100	10	1	.1	.01	.001	.000001	.000000001
Kilo	Hecto	Deka	Unit	Deci	Centi	Milli	Micro(μ)	Nano
km	hm	dkm	m	dm	cm	mm	μm	nm
kl	hl	dkl	l	dl	cl	mL	μl	nl
kg	hg	dkg	g	dg	cg	mg	μg	ng

☐ = a commonly used unit in science

Method: Changing Units in the Metric System

5.7 m = _____ cm   1. Determine whether you are changing from a larger to a smaller unit, or vice versa. Move left or right on the table accordingly. Ex. larger---> smaller = move decimal to the right.

5.7 m = _570_ cm   2. Use the table to determine how many places to move the decimal. Ex. m—> cm = 2 places

Milliliters, Cubic Centimeters (cc) and Grams

A very useful relationship to know in the metric system is:

 1 mL= 1 cc which weighs 1 g of water at standard temperature and pressure.

> ex.   50 mL = 50 cc which weigh 50 g (water)

Questions

1. What is the meter based on? liter? kilogram?
2. The metric system is based on which number?
3. List the prefixes less than 1 and indicate their value.
4. List the prefixes greater than 1 and indicate their value.
5. Do the metric conversion problems on your Lab Data Sheet.

Laboratory- Using the Metric System to Investigate Popcorn

Materials

250 mL graduated cylinder, popcorn, hot air popcorn popper, 10 mL graduated cylinder, metric ruler, balance, large container or bag to collect popcorn, heat gloves

Procedure

6. Mass the empty 10 mL graduated cylinder and record the mass in Table 1 on your Lab Data Sheet.
7. Measure a volume of 10 mL of popcorn in the 10 mL graduated cylinder and record in Table 2.
8. Mass the graduated cylinder and popcorn and record on your Lab Data Sheet in Table 1.
9. Select 10 seeds randomly from the 10 mL and measure their length in mm. Record the measurements in Table 3 on your Lab Data Sheet.
10. Return the 10 seeds to the graduated cylinder, pour all seeds into a hot air popper, and pop them, collecting the popped kernels in a bag.
11. Get a 250 mL beaker, mass it on the balance, and record in Table 1 on your Lab Data Sheet.
12. Wait until all (or nearly all) the kernels have popped, pour them into the 250 mL beaker, and mass the beaker and popcorn (and unpopped seeds) together. Record in Table 1.
13. Measure the volume of the cooked popcorn in mL and record in Table 2.
14. Select 10 pieces of cooked popcorn and measure the *greatest* length in mm. Record in Table 3.

Analysis

15. Find the average length of the cooked and uncooked popcorn and record in Table 3.
16. Find the cooked and uncooked masses and record in Table 1 on your Lab Data Sheet.

> **Method:**   container + popcorn(g) - container (g) = mass of popcorn (g)

17. a. What is the average length of the uncooked popcorn in cm? in m?
    b. How many cc of cooked popcorn did you get?
18. Find the % change in the mass, volume, and length of the cooked vs. uncooked popcorn and record in the designated spaces.

> **Method:** <u>Cooked popcorn (Avg. Mass, Volume, Length) - Uncooked Popcorn (Avg.M,V,L)</u>   X 100= % change
> Uncooked popcorn (Avg. Mass, Volume, Length)

19. Make a bar graph of the % change for volume, mass, and length.
20. Where was the greatest change--length, mass, or volume? Why?

Prelab

1. _____

_____

2. _____

3. _____

_____

4. _____

_____

5. a. 73.5cm = _____m   c. .0045dl =_____ l   e. 23, 758 mg= _____kg

    b. 1.45 hm= _____cm   d. 34.69dkg=_____ dg   f. .000034 kl= _____ cl

        g. 378 mL(water) = _____cc which weigh _____ g

Laboratory- Using the Metric System to Investigate Popcorn

6._____ 7. _____ 8. _____ 9. _____ 10. _____ 11. _____ 12. _____ 13. _____ 14. _____

Table 1.

	Mass of Graduated Cylinder + popcorn(g)	Mass of Graduated Cylinder (g)	Mass of Popcorn(g)
Uncooked			
	Mass of Beaker + Popcorn (g)	Mass of Beaker (g)	Mass of Popcorn(g)
Cooked			

% Change=_____

Table 2.

Uncooked Volume(mL)	Cooked Volume (mL)	% Change
10		

Table 3.

Uncooked Length (mm)	Cooked Length (mm)

Avg.=_____   Avg.=_____

% Change =_____

Analysis

15. _____

16. _____

17. a _____;_____

     b._____

18. _____

19. Graph

+

          Mass   Volume   Length

−

20. _____

Scientific Notation

Introduction

Scientific notation was developed so that the very large and very small numbers encountered in science could be written and manipulated more easily. For example, rather than writing that an organism has 450,000,000,000 cells (and having to count all the 0's), the same number can be expressed as 4.5×10^{11} cells.

The same system can be applied to very small numbers, as well. The size of one bacterium is .000003 m. The same number can be written more easily as 3.0×10^{-6} m.

Converting Standard Numbers into Scientific Notation
A simple two step procedure can be used to convert standard numbers into scientific notation.

1. Place the decimal point so that the number to be converted is between 1 and 10.
    Example a.   3472 = 3.472   Example b.   .000765 = 7.65

2. Count the number of spaces the decimal was moved.

Example a.
    3472 = 3.472   If the number is greater than one, the decimal will be moved to the left. The exponent 3 will be positive.

    3.472×10^3

Example b.
    .000765 = 7.65   If the number is between 0 and 1, the decimal will be moved to the right. The exponent 4 will be negative.

    7.65×10^{-4}

Converting Scientific Notation into Standard Numbers
1. Numbers greater than or equal to 1:

Example c.
    $7.05 \times 10^6 =$ _____   Starting at the decimal, count 6 places <u>to the right</u> and add the appropriate number of 0's.

    $7.05 \times 10^6 = 7,050,000$

2. Numbers greater than 0 and less than 1:
Example d.
    $4.767 \times 10^{-3} =$ _____   Starting at the decimal, count 3 places <u>to the left</u> and add the appropriate number of 0's.

    4.767 = .004767

Problems
1. Do the problems on your Lab Data Sheet converting from standard notation to scientific notation.
2. Do the problems on your Lab Data Sheet converting from scientific notation to standard notation.

Multiplying and Dividing with Exponents
In some applications it is necessary to multiply or divide with numbers in scientific notation.

1. When multiplying in scientific notation, you multiply the number, but add the exponents.

Example 1
$3.4 \times 10^4 \quad \times \quad 2.6 \times 10^2 = 3.4 \times 2.6 = 8.84 \quad ; \quad 10^4 \times 10^2 = 10^{4+2} = 10^6 \quad == \quad 8.84 \times 10^6$

2. When dividing in scientific notation, you divide the number but subtract the exponents.

Example 2
$8.2 \times 10^{14} / 4.6 \times 10^6 = 8.2/4.6 = 1.78 \quad ; \quad 10^{14} / 10^6 = 10^{14-6} = 10^8 \quad == \quad 1.78 \times 10^8$

Converting Units in the Metric System Using Scientific Notation
Both the metric system and scientific notation are based on 10.

Example 3
4.3×10^7 mm = _____ m

4.3×10^7 mm = __4.3×10^4__ m

1. There are 3 decimal places between mm and m.
2. mm --> m = smaller to larger unit; number must get smaller.
   Subtract exponents $10^{7-3} = 10^4$

Example 4
7.5×10^{-6} dm = _____ μm

7.5×10^{-6} dm = __7.5×10^{-1}__ μm

1. There are 5 decimal places between dm and μm.
2. dm --> μm = larger to smaller unit; number must get larger.
   Add exponents $10^{-6+5} = 10^{-1}$

Problems
3. Do the problems on your Lab Data Sheet multiplying and dividing exponents.
4. Do the problems on your LDS converting units in the metric system using scientific notation.

Activity- Using Scientific Notation to determine the Relative Size of Biological Entities

Materials
Calculator

5. Using the table on your Lab Data Sheet, convert all the lengths to meters in scientific notation.

6. Compare the lengths given in each statement.

Scientific Notation

Introduction

1. a. $345.89 =$ _____   d. $84,736 =$ _____   f. $294,728 =$ _____

   b. $.00034 =$ _____   e. $.0000000472 =$ _____   g. $23.004 =$ _____

   c. $345,000,000,000 =$ _____   h. $983,000,000 =$ _____

2. a. $2.49 \times 10^4 =$ _____   e. $4.52 \times 10^2 =$ _____

   b. $6.45 \times 10^7 =$ _____   f. $3.89 \times 10^{-5} =$ _____

   c. $5.28 \times 10^{-12} =$ _____   g. $3.49 \times 10^{-8} =$ _____

   d. $3.27 \times 10^6 =$ _____   h. $4.89 \times 10^{-5} =$ _____

3. a. 3.4×10^7 X $3.67 \times 10^2 =$ _____

   b. 4.56×10^3 X $7.6 \times 10^5 =$ _____

   c. 5.78×10^{-5} X $3.5 \times 10^2 =$ _____

   d. 2.56×10^2 X $4.5 \times 10^{-6} =$ _____

   e. 5.6×10^4 $\div$ $7.8 \times 10^6 =$ _____

   f. 4.67×10^{-6} $\div$ $3.8 \times 10^{-3} =$ _____

   g. 7.82×10^{-4} $\div$ $2.5 \times 10^8 =$ _____

   h. 5.9×10^{-5} $\div$ $5.8 \times 10^{-6} =$ _____

4. Use the metric system chart from 'Using the Metric System' if you need a reference.

   a. 4.5×10^{-3} cm $=$ _____ dm   e. 3.88×10^6 nm $=$ _____ m

   b. 4.7×10^5 µm $=$ _____ mm   f. 5.6×10^{-12} km $=$ _____ µm

   c. 2.8×10^3 mg $=$ _____ kg   g. 8.3×10^{-3} mg $=$ _____ g

   d. 3.4×10^8 mL $=$ _____ liter   h. 2.7×10^{14} m $=$ _____ km

Activity- Using Scientific Notation to determine the Relative Sizes of Biological Entities

Carbon atom= .2 nm   Tallest tree=112.ll m   Largest blue whale= 33.53 m

Avg. human height=167 cm   AIDS virus= 90 nm   *Tyrannosaurus rex*= 15.2 m

Escherichia coli= 2 µm   White Blood Cell= 15 µm

5. Convert all lengths listed above to meters _in scientific notation._

Item	Size in m (S.N.)	Item	Size in meters
Carbon Atom	_____	Largest Blue Whale	_____
Human Height	_____	White Blood Cell	_____
Escherichia coli	_____	*Tyrannosaurus rex*	_____
Tallest Tree	_____	AIDS virus	_____

6. Express answers in scientific notation.

   a. *E. coli* is _____times longer than an AIDS virus.

   b. A blue whale is _____times longer than a human being.

   c. 1 million AIDS viruses lined up would be _____m long.

   d. A white blood cell is _____times longer than an AIDS virus.

   e. A human being is _____times longer than a carbon atom.

   f. The blue whale is _____times longer than *T. rex*.

   g. The circumference of the earth is 39,000 km at the equator. How many people of average height would it take to span the circumference laying head to toe?

   h. The human body is composed of 11% Carbon. For every 12g of C there are 6.023×10^{23} atoms. How many atoms of C are there in a person with a mass of 50 kg?

68

Exploring Atoms

Introduction

<u>Atoms</u>

All physical entities are made of matter. Matter is anything which has mass and takes up space. There are three common states of matter--solid, liquid, and gas--on earth. A rare fourth form of matter here on earth, plasma, is actually the most abundant form of matter in the universe; it makes up the sun and other stars. A solid will have a definite fixed shape and volume. A liquid will have a definite volume, but will take the shape of its container. A gas has no fixed shape or volume.

Although the old Bohr model of the atom pictured below is extremely simplistic, and does not truly portray the appearance of an atom, it can serve as a starting point for the study of atoms.

An atom consists of neutrons and protons in a central nucleus being orbited by electrons. Neutrons have no charge and have a mass of approximately 1. Protons are positively charged and have a mass of approximately 1. Electrons orbiting around the nucleus have a charge of -1 and a mass only 1/1860 that of a proton or neutron. (Diagram 1)

Diagram 1

More than 99.9% of an atom's mass is centered in the nucleus. Atoms are mostly composed of empty space. If an atomic nucleus were enlarged to the size of a golf ball, the nearest electrons would be orbiting a kilometer away.

Electrons are located in discrete shells called orbitals. The first orbital away from the nucleus can hold 2 electrons, the next 8 electrons, and the next 8 or 18 electrons.

Questions

1. What is matter?
2. List and define the three common states of matter.
3. Draw and label an atom.
4. Where is most of an atom's mass located?

<u>Elements</u>

Elements are substances which can not be broken down into simpler parts. An element contains only one type of atom. There are 90 naturally occurring elements; this means they have been made by the fusion process in a star. Twenty five of the elements are found in living things, but only four--carbon, hydrogen, oxygen, and nitrogen--make up 96% of living tissue. Elements have been arranged by their characteristics into the Periodic Table of the Elements. The Periodic Table gives the atomic mass and atomic number of an element, and the number of protons, electrons, and neutrons of an element can be determined from the Table.

The atomic number is the number of protons in the nucleus. The atomic mass is the number of protons and neutrons added together. In an electrically neutral atom, the number of protons will equal the number of electrons, so the atomic number will also be an indication of the number of electrons. The number of neutrons can be determined by subtracting the atomic number (protons) from the atomic mass (protons + neutrons-- rounded to the nearest whole number).

Lithium (Diag. 2) has a rounded atomic mass (protons + neutrons) of 7 and an atomic number (protons) of 3. The number of electrons is equal to the number of protons = 3. The number of neutrons is calculated as 7 - 3 = 4.

3

Li

Atomic # = # of protons

Symbol for Lithium

Lithium
6.94

Questions   Diagram 2

5. What is an element?
6. Where are elements made?
7. How many elements are found in living things?
8. Which elements account for most of living tissue?
9. Where are elements organized?

Atomic Mass = protons and neutrons (Not an even number because of isotopes)

Isotopes and Ions (Diagram 3)

When an element gains or loses a proton, a different element is formed. For example, if one proton is added to mercury, gold is formed. However, there are two ways atoms can change but still remain the same element. If an atom gains or loses electrons, it becomes an **ion.** If the atom loses electrons, it becomes positively charged. If it gains electrons, it becomes positively charged. If an atom gains or loses neutrons, it becomes an **isotope**. While the charge on the atom does not change, the mass of the atom does change. Many isotopes such as ^{14}C are radioactive.

Diagram 3

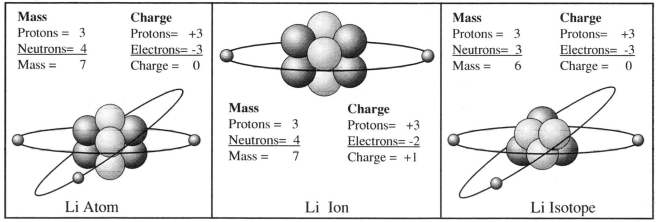

Mass	Charge
Protons = 3	Protons= +3
Neutrons= 4	Electrons= -3
Mass = 7	Charge = 0

Li Atom

Mass	Charge
Protons = 3	Protons= +3
Neutrons= 4	Electrons= -2
Mass = 7	Charge = +1

Li Ion

Mass	Charge
Protons = 3	Protons= +3
Neutrons= 3	Electrons= -3
Mass = 6	Charge = 0

Li Isotope

Questions

10. How is a different element formed?
11. Diagram and describe how an ion is formed.
12. Diagram and describe how an isotope is formed.
13. Analyze the Li atoms on your Lab Data Sheet and determine whether they are ions or isotopes.

Activity- Using the Periodic Table

Materials

Periodic Table of the Elements, pencil or pen

Procedure

14. Using a Periodic Table of the Elements, determine the number of protons, neutrons, and electrons in hydrogen, gold, carbon, and zinc. Record on your Lab Data Sheet.

Exploring Atoms

Introduction

1. _____

2. _____

_____

_____

3.

4. _____

5. _____

6. _____

7. _____

8. _____

9. _____

10. _____

11.

12.

13a. _____   13b. _____

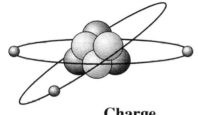

Mass
Protons = _____
Neutrons= _____
 Mass = _____

Charge
Protons = _____
Electrons= _____
Charge = _____

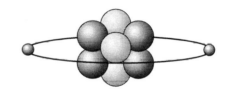

Mass
Protons = _____
Neutrons= _____
 Mass = _____

Charge
Protons = _____
Electrons= _____
Charge = _____

Activity- Using the Periodic Table

14.

Element	Protons	Electrons	Neutrons
Hydrogen			
Gold			
Carbon			
Zinc			

Measurements in Microscopy

Prelab

Any object observed under a microscope can be described with the word 'small', but precisely <u>how small</u> is critical information to many scientists. A millimeter, .001 of a meter, is typically used to measure small macroscopic objects, but even it is far too large a unit for microscopic measurements. The millimeter has been further divided into 1000 units called micrometers, which are abbreviated as μm. The Greek letter μ is used to symbolize micro, or 'millionth part of.' A micrometer is 1/1,000,000 of a meter. The μm is the most commonly used measurement in microscopy.

1 m = 1000 mm   **1mm= 1000 μm**

<u>Using mm and μm</u>

> Method: When changing from mm--> μm, or μm--> mm, three decimal places are moved.

Example:
  234 μm= _____mm   1. Determine if you are going from a larger -->smaller or
                       smaller --> larger unit. Here: smaller --> larger= move decimal left

  234 μm= __.234__ mm   2. Determine how many places to move the decimal. μm -->mm= 3

Questions
1. What is the unit of measurement used in microscopy?
2. What is its abbreviation?
3. How many are in 1 mm?
4. Do the problems on your Lab Data Sheet.

<u>Estimating the Size of an Object under the Microscope in μm</u>

> Method: To find the size of an object under the microscope:
>
> $$\frac{\text{μm in field of view}}{\text{number of objects across field}} = \text{size of one object}$$

Example: $\dfrac{1400\ \mu m}{5\ objects}$ =   280 μm / object

280 μm

Each object is approximately 280 μm long.

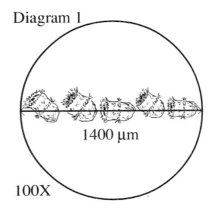

Diagram 1

1400 μm

100X

5. Do the size estimations on your Lab Data Sheet.

Laboratory- Determining the Size of Objects under the Microscope

Materials
Compound microscope with high and low power, clear plastic ruler with mm gradations, piece of paper for drawings, 4 prepared slides per group, calculator, 250-400 mL beakers for drawing circles optional--slides, cover slips, beaker with water, living organisms, dropper

Procedure
Finding the microscope's field of vision

6. Adjust the microscope so that the low power lens (usually 100X) is in place.

7. Place a clear plastic ruler on the stage and focus on the mm.

8. Visually determine how many mm fit across the diameter of the low power field of vision and record this on your Lab Data Sheet.

9. Calculate how many μm fit across the field of view and record it on your Lab Data Sheet.

10. Calculate how many μm fit across the high power field of vision. Record the high power field of vision of your microscope in μm on your Lab Data Sheet.

Method: To calculate the μm across the high power field of vision:

$$\frac{\text{Low power magnification}}{\text{High power magnification}} \quad X \quad \begin{matrix}\text{μm across low power} \\ \text{field of vision}\end{matrix} = \begin{matrix}\text{μm across high power} \\ \text{field of vision}\end{matrix}$$

Example: $\dfrac{100X}{400X}$ X   1400 μm =   = 350 μm across the high power field of vision

---

Estimating the Size of Objects under the Microscope

11. <u>On a separate piece of paper,</u> draw four different objects under low and high power. Label them with the **title**, **magnification**, and **size estimation in μm**.

12. Give size estimations in μm for each object for low and high power. Record on your Lab Data Sheet in Table 1.

Analysis
13. What happens to the field of view as the magnification increases?

14. Were your size estimates for the same object under low and high power close or far apart? Why?

Measurements in Microscopy

Prelab

1. _____

2. _____

3. _____

4.   a. 500µm =_____mm   c. 1.3 mm =_____µm

        b. 230 µm =_____mm   d. .62 mm=_____µm

5.

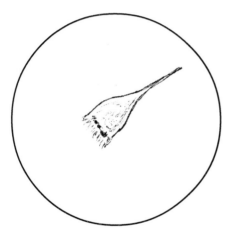

a. Field of Vision= 1400 µm
   Size=_____µm

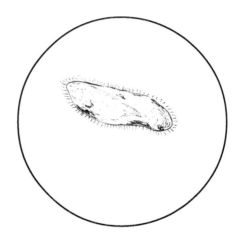

b. Field of Vision= 350 µm
   Size =_____µm

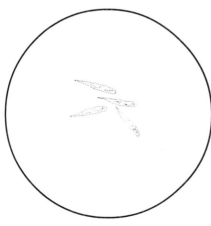

c. Field of Vision = 350 µm
   Size=_____ µm

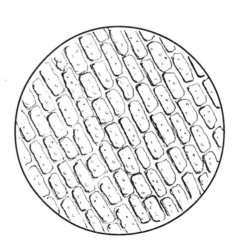

d. Field of Vision= 350 µm
   Length of plant cell=_____µm
   Width of plant cell =_____µm

Laboratory- Determining the Size of Objects under the Microscope

6. _____   7. _____

8. _____

9. _____

10. _____

11. _____

12.

Table 1.

Object	Size in μm	
	High Power	Low Power

Analysis

13. _____

14. _____

_____

Surface Area to Volume Ratio in Cells

Prelab

Surface Area-to-Volume Ratio in Cells

Living cells bring in food, water, and oxygen, and excrete wastes through the process of diffusion. Diffusion is the movement of molecules across a membrane from an area of higher concentration to an area of lower concentration. In this way, digested food molecules are absorbed into villi in the small intestine, and oxygen moves into and carbon dioxide out of lung cells.

Cells are dependent upon diffusion. They must have an adequate surface area to allow needed molecules in and unwanted molecules out fast enough to sustain their metabolism. A single cell which grows too large will not be able to take in sufficient food and oxygen or eliminate waste molecules fast enough. For this reason, large organisms have to be composed of many small cells.

Questions
1. What is diffusion?
2. How is diffusion used by living cells?
3. List two systems in vertebrates that are dependent on diffusion.
4. Why can't a single cell grow very large?
5. Why must large organisms be multicellular?

Finding Volume and Surface Area

Three dimensional objects will have a volume and surface area. Volume is measured in cubic units (cm^3) while surface area is measured in square units (cm^2).

Method

Example 1
Rectangular Solid

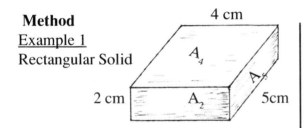

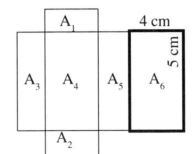

$A_6 = L \times W$
$A_6 = 5 \text{ cm} \times 4 \text{ cm}$
$A_6 = 20 \text{ cm}^2$

Volume = L x W x H
Volume = 5 cm x 4 cm x 2 cm
Volume = 40 cm^3

Total Surface Area = $A_1 + A_2 + A_3 + A_4 + A_5 + A_6$
Total Surface Area = $8cm^2 + 8cm^2 + 10cm^2 + 20cm^2 + 10cm^2 + 20cm^2$
= 76 cm^2

Example 2
Sphere

Volume = 4/3 πr^3
V = 4/3 (3.14) (8)
V = 33.5 cm^3

radius = 2 cm

Surface Area = 4 πr^2
SA = 4 (3.14) (4)
SA = 50.2 cm^2

radius = 2 cm

Calculating Surface Area to Volume Ratios

A ratio is the relation of two numbers, and it is used to compare numbers to each other. To find the surface area to volume ratio, make the surface area the numerator and the volume the denominator. Divide the numbers.

Example 1	Example 2
Surface Area/Volume = 76 / 40 = 1.9	Surface Area/ Volume = 50.2 / 33.5 = 1.5
(Units are not used to calculate the ratio.)	

Questions

6. Which of these two cells—Example 1 or Example 2— would have more diffusion? Why?

7. Does a cell need a high or low surface area to volume ratio? Why?

8-9. Do the problems on your Lab Data Sheet.

10. Rank order the SA/V ratios in problems 8 a/b and 9 a/b. Which cell is the most efficient? the least efficient? Why?

11. Formulate a hypothesis for the lab. Predict what will happen to the surface area to volume ratio as a baggie (cell) is filled with more and more water.

Laboratory- Surface Area / Volume Ratio in a Growing 'Cell'

Materials

Plastic baggie (cell), string, ruler, 100 mL graduated cylinder, water, calculator

Procedure

12. Fill the corner of a baggie with 100 mL of water, and do not seal it. Hold the baggie so that one corner holds the water. (Diagram 1)

13. Measure the circumference in cm at the widest point with a string and record on your LDS.   Diagram 1

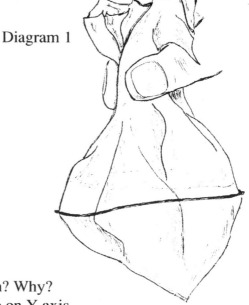

14. Fill the baggie with another 100 mL of water (total =200 mL), and measure the circumference in cm.

15. Repeat Step 13 for 300 mL and 400 mL.

16. Calculate the surface area for each 'cell' using the formulas for a sphere.

17. Calculate the SA/V ratio for each cell and record.

Analysis

18. Which 'cell' would have the most efficient diffusion? Why?

19. Graph the volume on the X axis vs. the SA/V ratio on Y axis.

   19a. What happens to the SA/V ratio as the cell's volume grows larger?

20. Using the information from the graph, explain why cells are small.

Surface Area to Volume Ratio

Prelab

1. _____

2. _____

3. _____

4. _____

5. _____

6. _____

7. _____

8. Calculate the surface area to volume ratios for these two rectangular solids:
   a) 2 cm x   3 cm x   4 cm

   b) 6 μm x 8 μm x 10 μm (Watch the units!!)

9. Calculate the surface area to volume ratios for these two spheres:
   a) radius= 4 cm

   b) *diameter*= 1.5 mm (Watch d and r!)

10. _____

_____

11. _____

Laboratory- Surface Area to Volume Ratio in a Growing 'Cell'

Table 1.

12. _____   15. _____

13. _____   16. _____

14. _____   17. _____

Volume (mL)	Circumference (cm)	Radius $(C/\pi)/2$	Surface Area $(4\pi r^2)$	SA/V ratio
100				
200				
300				
400				

Analysis

18. _____

_____

19.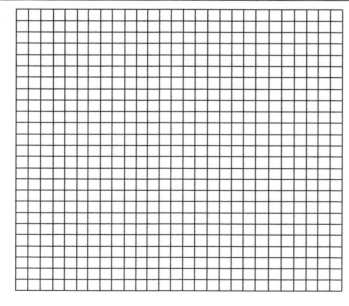

19a. _____

_____

_____

20. _____

Diffusion in Potatoes

Prelab

Plant and animal cells use diffusion to acquire or eliminate substances needed to maintain their metabolism. Oxygen diffuses into and carbon dioxide out of the lungs, and the products of digestion diffuse across the microvilli of the small intestine. Diffusion of a substance occurs from an area of higher concentration to an area of lower concentration. No energy is used in diffusion.

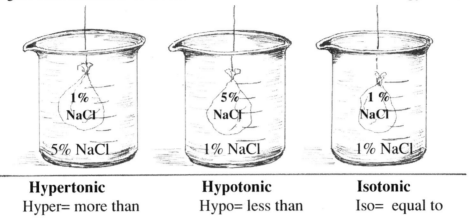

Hypertonic	Hypotonic	Isotonic
Hyper= more than	Hypo= less than	Iso= equal to

Solute Movement

A **solute** is a dissolved solid in a **solvent**, the liquid part of the solution. The terms **hypertonic**, **hypotonic**, and **isotonic** are used to describe solute concentrations on two sides of a membrane. These terms are relative; that is, one solution is hypertonic, hypotonic, or isotonic compared to another. In the hypertonic example, the solute concentration (NaCl) outside is greater than the solute concentration inside--5% > 1%. Assuming the membrane is permeable to salt, the salt will diffuse into the bag, from an area of higher to an area of lower concentration. In the hypotonic example, the salt concentration is lower outside the bag than inside-- 1% < 5%. Here, salt will diffuse from the inside to the outside. In the isotonic example, there will be an equal movement of salt across the bag membrane in both directions--1% = 1%. The net movement of salt will be equal.

Solvent Movement

Solute movement across the bag membrane is only one part of the story. The liquid part of the solution--the solvent--will also diffuse. In the **hypertonic** example, there is 95% solvent and 5% solute outside compared to 99% solvent and 1% solute inside. The water (solvent) will move from an area of higher concentration inside to an area of lower concentration outside. Since there is much more water than salt, the bag will shrink. In the **hypotonic** example, the water concentration is higher outside (99%) than inside (95%), so the water will diffuse into the bag, and it will swell. Net movement of water in the **isotonic** example will be equal. The diffusion of water is called **osmosis.**

Questions

1. What is diffusion? Is energy used?
2. What does hypertonic mean? hypotonic? isotonic?
3. What is a solvent? solute?
4. What is osmosis?
5a-5b. Do the problems on your Lab Data Sheet.
6. Write a hypothesis for the Lab. What do you think will happen to the length, mass, and volume of the potato cores in different concentrations of sugar water?

Laboratory- Effect of Different Concentrations of Sugar Water on Potato Cores

Materials
White potato, razor blade, metric ruler, balance, labels, paper towels, aluminum foil or plastic wrap, large test tubes, test tube rack, 10% and 20% sugar solutions, distilled water, cork borers

Procedure -- *Day 1*
7. Using a cork borer, cut three cores from a potato. Trim off the skin.
8. Trim each core so that its length will be exactly 3.0 cm and record this measurement in Table 1 on your Lab Data Sheet.
9. Measure the diameter of each core and record it in Table 1.
10. Find the mass of each core using a balance. Record the mass to the nearest .1 g in Table 1.
11. Find the volume of each core and record in Table 1 and on the board.

 Method: Volume of a Cylinder
 Volume of a cylinder = $\pi r^2 h$
Example: Diameter= 1.1 cm; Height= 3.0 cm.

Volume = 3.14 x (.55 cm)^2 x 3.0 cm

Volume = 2.849 cm^3 = 2.85 cm^3

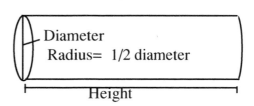

Diameter
Radius= 1/2 diameter

Height

---

12. Place each core in a different test tube and label them A, B, and C.
13. Pour distilled water into tube A until it covers the core by 1 cm.
14. Pour 10% sugar water into tube B until it covers the core, and 20% sugar water into tube C until it covers the core by 1 cm.
15. Wrap the top of each tube with foil and store in a test tube rack until the next day.

Day 2
16. Find the length, mass, and volume of each core and record it in Table 1 on your Lab Data Sheet.

Analysis
17. Find the length, mass, and volume difference (Δ = difference) between Day 1 and Day 2. (subtract--Note: Some might be negative!!)

Graphing
18. Graph the difference (Δ) between Day 1 and Day 2 masses, volumes, and lengths vs. sugar water concentrations.
   a. Notice where the line on the mass graph crosses the 0 line. This is the sugar solution that is isotonic to the potato cells. Record it in your lab notebook.

19. What overall relationship exists between the concentration of sugar water and the changes in potato core lengths, masses, and volumes?

20. Relate the gains and losses in the potato core lengths, masses, and volumes to osmosis. Why did the gains and losses occur in water or concentrations of sugar water?

82

Diffusion in Potatoes

Prelab

1. _____ ; _____

_____

2. _____

_____

_____

3. _____

_____

4. _____

5a-5b. Describe the following situations. What will happen to the bags, assuming they are
permeable to sugar and water? Why?

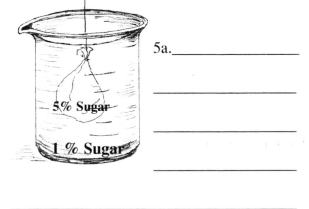

5a._____

_____

_____

_____

_____

5b. _____

_____

_____

_____

_____

6._____

_____

Laboratory- Diffusion in Potatoes

7. _____   8. _____   9. _____   10._____   11. _____   12. _____   13. _____

14._____ 15. _____ 16. _____

Table 1.

Measurements	Core A (0% Sugar)			Core B(10% Sugar)			Core C (20% Sugar)		
	Day 1	Day 2	Differ.= Δ	Day 1	Day 2	Differ.=Δ	Day 1	Day 2	Differ.=Δ
Length (cm)									
Mass (g)									
Diameter(cm) radius(cm)									
Volume(cm³)									

Analysis

17. _____

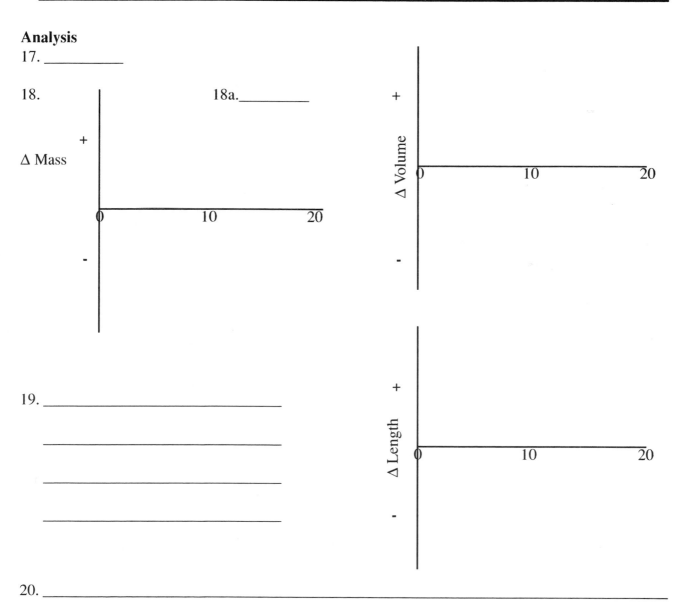

18.   18a._____

Δ Mass
+
0   10   20
-

Δ Volume
+
0   10   20
-

Δ Length
+
0   10   20
-

19. _____

_____

_____

_____

20. _____

_____

Enzymes and the Rate of Reaction

Prelab

Enzymes are large protein molecules which act as biological catalysts--they speed up biochemical reactions in the body. The molecule with which an enzyme reacts is called a substrate. Enzymes are very specific; they react only with their unique substrate. When enzymes were discovered, fast chemical reactions in the body (which took place slowly in test tubes) could be explained. Enzymes speed up biochemical reactions by lowering the energy of activation of their substrates.

Catalase

Catalase is an enzyme which converts hydrogen peroxide into water and oxygen. The substrate for catalase--hydrogen peroxide (H_2O_2)--is a product of cellular metabolism which can poison cells.

$$H_2O_2 \xrightarrow{\quad catalase \quad} H_2O + O_2 \uparrow$$

If hydrogen peroxide were allowed to build up even over a short period of time it would kill the cell. Catalase has to work very quickly to ensure that hydrogen peroxide concentrations remain low.

The Rate of Reaction

The rate of reaction of an enzyme can be measured to determine how fast the enzyme is converting substrate into product. A rate is the speed at which something occurs during a certain time period. Examples include 20 mL per second (20 mL/sec) and 1.5 µl per minute (1.5 µl/min).

Rates are calculated using the formula: $\dfrac{y_2 - y_1}{x_2 - x_1}$

Example:

Sucrase is an enzyme which converts sucrose into glucose and fructose. The following data for glucosewere taken in an experiment. What is the reaction rate for sucrase between 30 and 45 seconds?

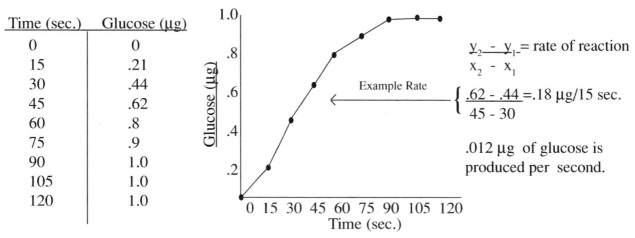

Time (sec.)	Glucose (µg)
0	0
15	.21
30	.44
45	.62
60	.8
75	.9
90	1.0
105	1.0
120	1.0

$\dfrac{y_2 - y_1}{x_2 - x_1} =$ rate of reaction

$\dfrac{.62 - .44}{45 - 30} = .18$ µg/15 sec.

.012 µg of glucose is produced per second.

Example Rate

Questions
1. What is an enzyme?
2. What is catalase? What is the substrate for catalase? Write the catalase reaction.
3. What is a rate? How is the rate calculated?
4. Do the reaction rate problem on your Lab Data Sheet.
5. Hypothesis: Rank the rate of reaction for catalase-hydrogen peroxide for seconds 0-10, 10-20, 20-30, 30-40, and 40-60 in terms of slow, medium, fast, or 0.

Laboratory- A Simulation: The Reaction Rate of Catalase and Hydrogen Peroxide

Materials
Per group of 4 students: 30 mLs of fresh 3% hydrogen peroxide, 30 mLs of liver water mixture, 100 mL graduated cylinder, 10 mL graduated cylinder, 250 mL Erlenmeyer flask, glass tube in rubber stopper which fits the Erlenmeyer flask, 40 cm long rubber tubing which fits the glass tube, water tub, stop watch, **goggles**

Procedure
6. Assemble the equipment shown in Diagram 1.

7. Fill the tub approximately 3/4 with water.

8. Measure 10 mLs of H_2O_2 and pour it into the 250 mL Erlenmeyer Flask.

9. Carefully measure out 10 mL's of the liver water mixture.

10. Dip the 100 mL graduated cylinder into the water until it is full, then invert it (Diag 1.) *Allow no bubbles in the cylinder.* Insert the rubber tubing inside the bottom of the graduated cylinder, *again allowing no air bubbles!* Assign one person to hold the tubing in place.

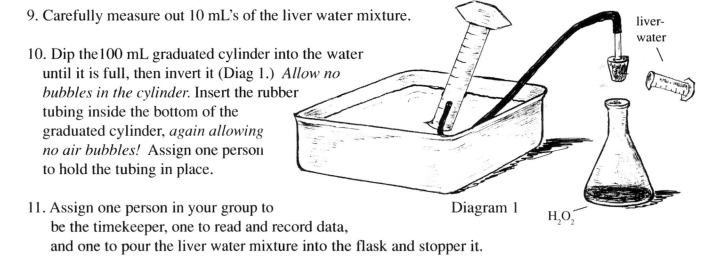

liver-water

Diagram 1 H_2O_2

11. Assign one person in your group to be the timekeeper, one to read and record data, and one to pour the liver water mixture into the flask and stopper it.

And now, get ready for quick action!!!!!!
12. Pour the liver water mixture into the flask <u>quickly</u> and <u>immediately</u> stopper the flask.

13. The timekeeper calls off every five seconds and the data collector reads and records how much oxygen gas has been produced in Table 1 on the Lab Data Sheet.

14. Repeat steps 8-14 twice more and write your average O_2 volumes on the Lab Data Sheet. Repeat as often as necessary to obtain three good trials of data.

Analysis
15. Calculate the average mL's of oxygen produced and record in Table 1.
16. Graph the average mL's of oxygen vs. time (secs) on Graph 1.
17. <u>Using the averages,</u> calculate on a separate piece of paper rates for seconds 0-10, for seconds 10-20, for seconds 20-30, for seconds 30-40 and for seconds 40-60. Record and rank them in order in Table 2.
18. Why is the graph of an enzyme-substrate reaction shaped like it is? Describe in terms of reaction rates.

Enzymes and the Rate of Reaction *Laboratory Data Sheet*

Prelab

1. _____

_____

2. _____ ; _____

_____

3. _____

_____

4. The following data were collected in a catalase-hydrogen peroxide experiment. Graph the data and calculate the rates of the reaction for seconds 0-20, 20-40, and 40-60.

Time (sec.)	O$_2$ Produced (mL)
0	0
5	24
10	36
15	39
20	42
25	47
30	50
35	53
40	53
45	53
50	53
55	53
60	53

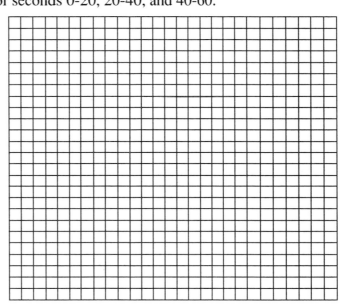

Rate of reaction for seconds a) 0-20=_____ b) 20-40= _____ c) 40-60=_____

5. Hypothesis- Seconds 0-10= _____ 10-20=_____ 20-30= _____

Seconds 30-40=_____ 40-60=_____

Laboratory- A Simulation: The Reaction Rate of Catalase and Hydrogen Peroxide

6. _____ 7._____ 8. _____ 9._____ 10. _____

11._____ 12. _____ 13._____ 14._____ 15. _____

Table 1.

	Trial 1	Trial 2	Trial 3	Average (mL)
Time (sec)	0₂ Produced (mL)	0₂ Produced (mL)	0₂ Produced (mL)	0₂ Produced (mL)
0	0	0	0	0
5				
10				
15				
20				
25				
30				
35				
40				
45				
50				
60				

Analysis

16. _____

17.

Table 2.

Seconds	Rate	Rank
0-10		
10-20		
20-30		
30-40		
40-60		

Graph 1

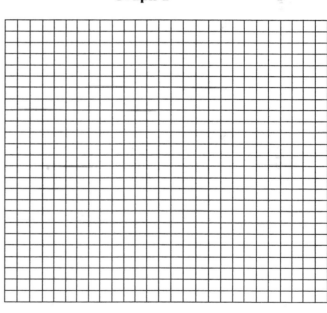

18. _____

_____

_____

_____

^{14}C Age Determination

Introduction

Radioactivity and Half-Life

Atoms are composed of protons, neutrons, and electrons. When the number of protons in an element changes, a new element is created. If the number of electrons changes, an ion results. If the number of neutrons varies, an isotope is produced which changes the atomic mass. Often a different number of neutrons makes the isotope unstable, causing the nucleus to disintegrate spontaneously into more stable elements. Atoms with unstable nuclei are called radioactive. Three types of radiation, including two types of particles-- alpha (α) and beta (β)--and one type of high energy photon -- gamma (γ)-- are emitted by such unstable nuclei.

The overall rate of decay of a radioactive isotope into stable elements is measured using the half life. This is the time it takes for half of a given amount of a radioactive isotope to change into stable elements. For example, Uranium has a half life of 4.5 billion years while the element Californium has a half life of 45 minutes. They both decay into smaller, more stable elements.

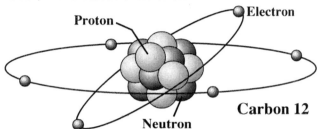

Carbon 12 and Carbon 14

Carbon 12 is the most common form of Carbon. It will have 6 protons, 6 neutrons, and 6 electrons. Carbon has four electrons in its outer orbital, and it can form four bonds to other atoms or molecules.

However, approximately 1.3 x 10^{-12} of Carbon atoms are ^{14}C, an unstable, radioactive isotope containing two extra neutrons. ^{14}C is produced when cosmic rays interact with the atmosphere, and it has a half life of 5730 years. This means that after 5730 years one kg of ^{14}C would be converted into 500 g of Nitrogen gas with 500 g of ^{14}C remaining. After 11,460 years, one half of the remaining 500g of ^{14}C would have become Nitrogen, so 250 g of ^{14}C would remain. After another 5730 years, 125 g of the original amount of ^{14}C would remain, and so on.

Assimilation of Carbon 14

Almost all living things will assimilate radioactive ^{14}C during their lifetimes. After death, this accumulated ^{14}C begins to decay at a steady rate, eventually becoming Nitrogen. When an old organic object is found, the ratio of ^{14}C to ^{12}C is determined and compared to that in a similar living organism. The age of the object can then be determined from a graph of the half life of ^{14}C. After about 60,000 years, the amount of ^{14}C is so small that it cannot be detected.

Questions
1. How is a new element produced? an ion? an isotope?
2. What causes an element to be radioactive? What are the radioactive particles?
3. What is the half life of a radioactive substance?
4. What is ^{14}C? How is it produced and what is its half life?
5. Explain how to find the age of an old organic fossil containing ^{14}C.
6. Can the age of the fossil bone of a dinosaur be determined using the Carbon 14 dating method? Why or why not?

Activity- Determining the Age of Old Organic Objects

Materials
Pencil or pen, ruler

Procedure
7. Fill in Table 1 on the Lab Data Sheet.

8. Using the information from Table 1, construct a graph of ^{14}C half life(years) vs. the ^{14}C to ^{12}C ratio.
     a. X axis = ^{14}C half life(years) **Start with 0, then 5730, then 11, 460, etc.**
     b. Y axis= ^{14}C to ^{12}C ratio **Start with 0, then use intervals of .05 <u>until you reach 1.</u>**
     c. Plot the points, starting with 0,1; 5730, .5; etc. Connect the points with a smooth line.

9. After constructing the graph on your Lab Data Sheet, use interpolation to determine the age of the objects listed in Table 2.

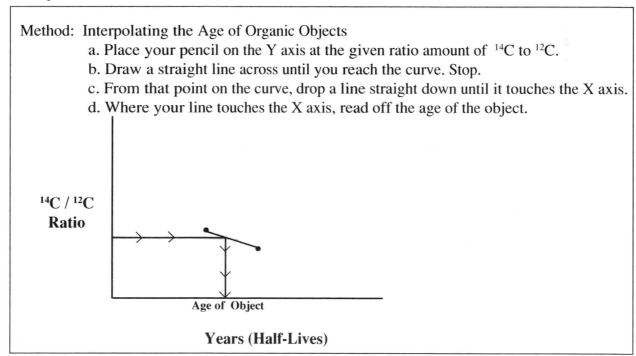

Method: Interpolating the Age of Organic Objects
     a. Place your pencil on the Y axis at the given ratio amount of ^{14}C to ^{12}C.
     b. Draw a straight line across until you reach the curve. Stop.
     c. From that point on the curve, drop a line straight down until it touches the X axis.
     d. Where your line touches the X axis, read off the age of the object.

^{14}C / ^{12}C **Ratio**

Age of Object

Years (Half-Lives)

Questions

10. What shape does the graph of Carbon 14 take? Why?

11. What are the strengths of this method to determine the age of old organic objects? the limitations?

^{14}C Age Determination

Introduction

1. _____

_____

_____

2. _____

_____

3. _____

_____

4. _____

_____

5. _____

_____

6. _____

_____

Activity- Determining the Age of Old Organic Objects

7.

Table 1.

^{14}C to ^{12}C Ratio	Half Lives	Years
1.0	0	0
.5	1	5730
.25	2	11,460
	3	
.063	4	
	5	
.016	6	

8.

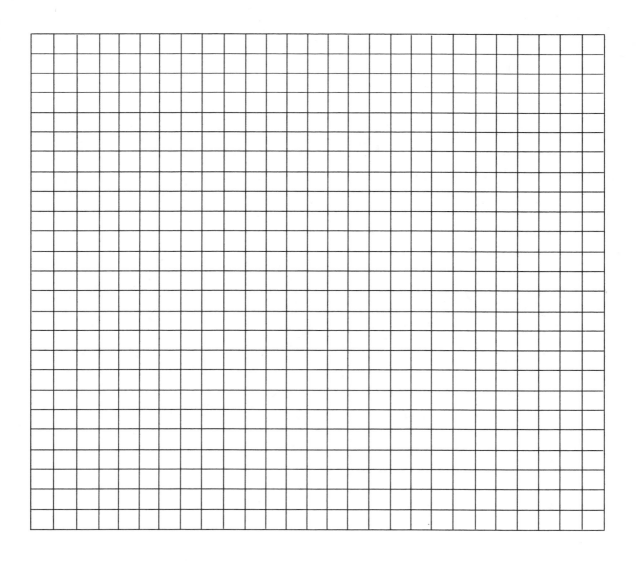

9.

Table 2.

Determine the age of the
following objects from the
their ¹⁴C content. Use your
graph above to interpolate.

Object	¹⁴C/ ¹²C Ratio	Estimated Age
1	.06	
2	.30	
3	.57	
4	.89	

Questions

10._____

11. _____

Pigment Chromatography

Prelab

<u>Visible Light:</u>

Visible light, also called white light, is composed of many different colors, or wavelengths. In turn, visible light makes up only a fraction of the overall Electromagnetic Spectrum, pictured below.

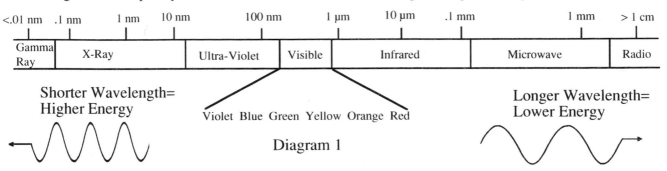

Diagram 1

<u>Plant Pigments</u>

Plants use only a small portion of visible light for photosynthesis. Their leaves contain pigments, molecules which absorb discrete wavelengths (colors) of light. Photosynthetic pigments absorb the wavelengths of blue and red best, then transfer the captured light energy to the reactions of photosynthesis. Pigments also reflect certain colors, which is why pigments can appear green or yellow.

Questions

1. What is another name for white light?
2. Draw the Electromagnetic Spectrum, indicating where visible light fits in.
3. What is a pigment?
4. Do pigments reflect the same color they absorb? Explain.
5. Which wavelengths (colors) do plants absorb best?

<u>Chromatography</u>

Molecules of different solubilities can be separated out of solution using special solvents. The most soluble molecules will be carried by the solvent the furthest. This process of separation is called chromatography.

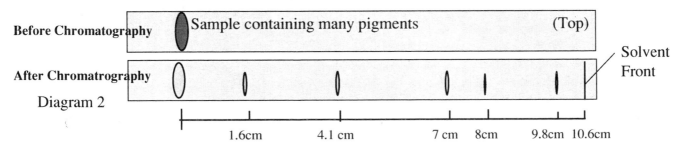

Diagram 2

R_f values- The R_f value represents the ratio of the distance the pigment travelled compared to the solvent front. Each plant pigment has a distinct value which can be used to identify it.

The R_f is calculated by dividing the distance each band moves by the distance the solvent front moves. The R_f value will then always be between 0 and 1.

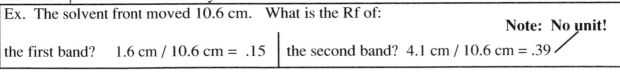

Ex. The solvent front moved 10.6 cm. What is the Rf of:

Note: No unit!

the first band? 1.6 cm / 10.6 cm = .15 | the second band? 4.1 cm / 10.6 cm = .39

Questions

6. Calculate the R_f's for the three remaining bands and write them on your Lab Data Sheet.
7. How does chromatography work?

Laboratory- Separation of Photosynthetic Pigments using Chromatography
Materials
Large test tube, fitted rubber stopper, pin or paper clip, chromatography solvent, ruler, chromatography paper, spinach leaf, paper towel, 10p finishing nail, goggles

Procedure
8. Cut a piece of chromatography paper which fits the length of the test tube.

9. Lay the chromatography strip on a paper towel.

10. Place the spinach leaf over one end of the strip. With the dull end of the nail, punch a stripe of chlorophyll onto the chromatography paper 2.5 cm above the end of the paper.

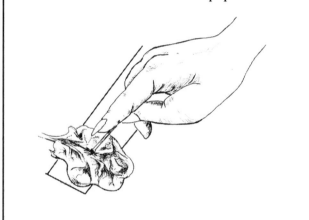

11. Repeat this process two more times using a different part of the leaf.

12. Turn the chromatography paper over and repeat three times.

13. Pour 1 cm of chromatography solution into the test tube.

14. Attach the chromatography strip to the stopper and place it into the tube.

   Stopper tightly!!

   Make sure the chlorophyll spot does not touch the solvent.

   The stripe must be concentrated.

   Solvent

15. Let the solvent move until it is about 1 cm from the top of the paper (15-25 mins.)

16. Remove the strip and measure the distances from the original stripe to the *solvent front first*, then the pigment bands. *Return the unused solvent quickly to its container.*

17. Draw the bands in your lab notebook with the correct distances.

18. Calculate the R_f values for the various bands and record in Table 1 on your Lab Data Sheet.

Analysis

19. How many bands were there? What are the colors? Why do plants have different pigments?
20. What does each band represent?
21. Why can pigments be separated?
22. Compare your R_f values with the actual values on the board and name each band.

Pigment Chromatography

Prelab

1. _____

2.

3. _____

4. _____

5. _____

6.

   Rf =_____   Rf=_____   Rf =_____

7. _____

Laboratory- Separation of Photosynthetic Pigments using Chromatography

8. _____ 9. _____ 10. _____

11. _____ 12. _____ 13. _____

14. _____ 15. _____ 16. _____

17. _____

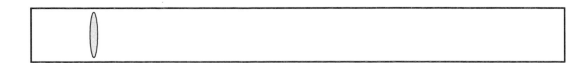

18. _____

Table 1.

Band #	Color	Distance (cm)	Rf
Solvent Front			
1			
2			
3			
4			

Analysis

19. _____

_____

_____

20. _____

21. _____

22. _____

_____

_____

_____

Measuring pH in *Zygocactus*

Prelab

pH is the measure of acidity/alkalinity (base) of a substance. The pH system is based on the Hydrogen ion (H^+) concentration in the solution. The pH ranges from 0 to 14, with 0 being strongly acidic, 14 being strongly alkaline, and 7 being neutral.

1	more H+	7	more OH-	14
Acid		Neutral		Basic (Alkaline)

pH Determination

The pH number is actually based on a power of 10—a logarithm, which indicates the Hydrogen ion concentration $[H^+]$. A pH 1= $[H^+]$ of 10^{-1}, pH 3= $[H^+]$ of 10^{-3}, etc. Remember, -1 > -3, so a pH 1 has more Hydrogen ions and is a stronger acid than a pH 3. See Diagram 1 below.

Diagram 1.
Relative Hydrogen Ion
Concentration between
pH 1 - 3.

pH 1	pH 2	pH 3
$[H+]= 10^{-1}$	$[H+] = 10^{-2}$	$[H+]= 10^{-3}$

Since pH is based on powers of 10, a pH 1 is 10 times stronger acid than a pH 2, a pH 2 is 10 times stronger acid than a pH 3, etc. A pH 1 is 100 times stronger acid than a pH 3, a pH 4 is 100 times stronger acid than a pH 6, etc. The pH is determined by finding the -log of the Hydrogen ion concentration $[H+]$. This shows the amount of Hydrogen ions (H^+) available:

$$pH = -\log [H+] \quad \text{and} \quad [H^+] = 10^{-pH} \quad \text{example:} \quad pH 1 = -\log 0.1 \text{ and } 0.1 = 10^{-1}$$

Examples:

a. What is the pH of a solution with a $[H^+]$ of 10^{-4}? $10^{-9.6}$?	c. How much stronger is an acid of pH 3 than an acid of pH 5?
$-\log 10^{-4} = pH 4$; $-\log 10^{-9.6} = pH 9.6$	pH 3 = $[10^{-3}]$ pH 5= $[10^{-5}]$ $[10^{-3}] - [10^{-5}] =$
b. What is the $[H+]$ of a substance with a pH of a) 6? b) 7.4?	$[10^{-3}] + [10^{+5}] = [10^{+2}] = 100$ times stronger
	d. How much stronger is a base of pH 11.7 than 9.5?
1) pH= 6 = $-\log 6 = [10^{-6}] = [H+]$	$[10^{-9.5}] - [10^{-11.7}]$
2) pH= 7.4 = $-\log 7.4 = [10^{-7.4}] =[H+]$	$[10^{-9.5}] + [10^{+11.7}] = [10^{2.2}]$ antilog of 2.2 = 158.5

Questions

1.-8. Do the problems on your Lab Data Sheet.

Crassulacean Acid Metabolism (CAM) in *Zygocactus*
Plants in the family Crassulaceae have adapted to dry climates by closing their stomata during the day, which is opposite of most C_3 plants. This is beneficial to survival since less water is lost through transpiration. When the stomata are open at night, CO_2 is fixed and then passed through a series of organic acids, eventually arriving at the Calvin Cycle. This process is called Crassulacean Acid Metabolism.

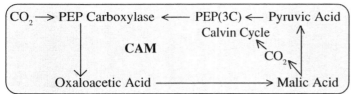

The *Zygocactus*, also known as the Christmas Cactus, can be used to demonstrate CAM. The pH can vary two points from morning to evening. At night CO_2 is taken in, so the pH will be lower, reflecting a higher acid concentration.

Throughout the day the plant deacidifies and by evening the pH is higher.

Questions
9. When do CAM plants open their stomata? Why?
10. What is being taken in by CAM plants and fixed into organic acids?
11. What is the ultimate destination of the CO_2?

Laboratory- Measuring pH in *Zygocactus*
Materials
Per class- One *Zygocactus*(Diagram 2) with at least 50 leaves. Per Group- clamp, pH meter, 2 standardized buffers at different pH, deionized water, one 50-mL beaker, mortar and pestle, cheesecloth.

Procedure (per group)
Taking pH measurements:
12. Calibrate the pH meter using buffers of known pH.
13. Remove one leaf from the *Zygocactus* and grind it up in the mortar and pestle (Diagram 3).
14. Add 10 mL's of distilled water, and strain the mixture through cheesecloth into a 50 mL beaker (Diagram 4).
15. Insert the pH meter (Diagram 5) and record the pH on the board for the correct time time of day. Record the class average in Table 1.

(The pH will be measured once an hour throughout the day by other classes and once in the late afternoon/ early evening.

Next Day   Next Day   Next Day
16. Record the average pH measurements from the other classes on your Lab Data Sheet in Table 1.

Analysis
17. Graph the average pH vs. time for the Zygocactus.
18. When did the *Zygocactus* have low pH? high pH? Why?
19. What was the highest pH? Lowest pH?
20. How much stronger was the acid at the lowest vs. the highest pH?

Diagram 2

Diagram 3

Diagram 4

Diagram 5

Measuring pH in *Zygocactus*

Prelab

1. What is the $[H^+]$ of pH 5? _____

2. What is the pH if $[H^+] = 10^{-3.4}$? _____

3. What is the pH if $[H^+] = 10^{-11}$? _____

4. What is the $[H^+]$ of pH 6.62? _____

5. A pH 2.5 is how much stronger than pH 5.5 acid? _____

6. A pH 3 acid is how much stronger than pH 6 acid? _____

7. How much stronger is a base of pH 13 than a base of pH 9? _____

8. How much stronger is a base of pH 10.6 than a base of 8.2? _____

9. _____

10. _____

11. _____

Laboratory - Measuring pH in *Zygocactus*

12. _____

13. _____

14. _____

15. _____

16. _____   **Table 1.**

Time(Hrs.)	0	1	2	3	4	5	6	7	Late Afternoon/ Early Evening
pH									

Analysis

17._____

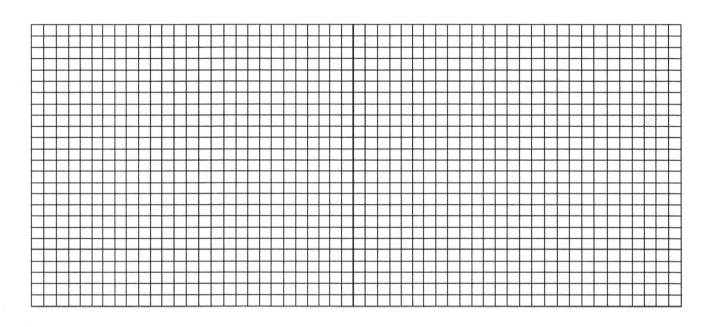

18. _____

19. _____

20. _____

The Effectiveness of Antibiotics and Antiseptics

Prelab

Although most bacteria are benign to human beings, a few types called pathogens cause much human disease. Killing pathogenic bacteria in the body as well as on surfaces is important to health. Antibiotics are substances which prevent the growth of or kill bacteria which have already invaded the body. They are the natural waste products of the metabolism of certain fungi and bacteria. Antiseptics kill bacteria on surfaces such as table tops, floors, or even in the mouth.

Bacteria will grow well in sterile petri dishes which contain the nutrients they need. The nutrients have been mixed with powdered agar, a derivative of seaweed. The medium is heated to sterilize it, then allowed to cool where it looks like gelatin. Bacteria are then spread onto these agar containing 'plates' using sterile technique. An absorbent disk containing an antibiotic or antiseptic is placed on the agar. If the antibiotic or antiseptic is effective against the bacteria, a **ring of inhibition** will be seen on the plate. This is a clear area where no bacteria can grow.

Questions
1. What is a pathogen?
2. What are antibiotics? Where do they come from?
3. What is an antiseptic?
4. What is a ring of inhibition?

Laboratory- The Effectiveness of Antibiotics and Antiseptics against *E. Coli*
Materials
per group- Bunsen Burner, *E. coli*. in Luria Broth Base, 2 LB 'plates,' petri dishes, glass spreader, .1 mL pipette, alcohol, 3 antibiotics, 3 antiseptics, forceps, Control discs (in sterile water), marker
***Caution**-- Always follow sterile technique procedures when working with bacteria. Never touch bacteria on plates directly. Wash your hands thoroughly with disinfectant soap after this lab.*

Procedure
5. Get two plates for your group. Label one 'Antibiotics' and the other one 'Antiseptics.'

6. *Keeping the 'plate' tightly closed to prevent contamination,* divide the <u>bottom</u> into 4 sections, called quadrants. Label 3 of the quadrants with the initials of 3 different antibiotics. Label the 4th quadrant with the letter 'C' for control. (Diagram 1)

7. *Keeping the second plate tightly closed to prevent contamination,* divide the bottom into 4 sections. Label 3 of the quadrants with the initials of different antiseptics. Label the 4th quadrant with 'C.' (Diag. 1)

8. Use sterile technique to spread bacteria onto both the plates.
   a. Dip the glass spreader in alcohol and immediately move through flame.
   b. Let the flame go out and touch the spreader to the agar.
   c. Vortex shake and remove .1 mL of bacteria and put on the agar. Spread with a glass spreader.

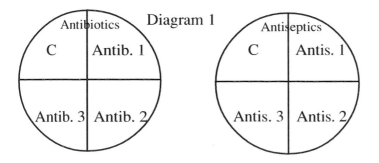

Diagram 1

Antibiotics: C | Antib. 1 / Antib. 3 | Antib. 2

Antiseptics: C | Antis. 1 / Antis. 3 | Antis. 2

Antibiotics

9. Use the appropriate antibiotic dispenser to place each of 3 different discs on the correct quadrant. *Open the plate approximately 2-3 cm, place the disc and quickly close to prevent contamination.*

10. Dip the tips of forceps into alcohol, and quickly pass it through a flame. After the flame has gone out, pick up a Control disc and place it onto the appropriate quadrant. *Open the plate approximately 2-3 cm and quickly close to prevent contamination.* (Diagram 2)

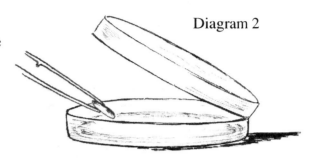
Diagram 2

Antiseptics

11. Dip the tips of forceps into alcohol, and quickly pass it through a flame. After the flame has gone out, pick up an antiseptic disc and place it onto the appropriate quadrant. *Open the plate approximately 2-3 cm and quickly close to prevent contamination.*

12. Repeat for the other two antiseptics and Control disc, then seal the plates with tape.

13. Place the plates <u>upside down</u> in an incubator at 37 °C for 72 hours.

Analysis --After 72 Hours
Caution: It is not necessary to open the plates to measure the rings of inhibition!

14. Measure the widest diameter of the ring of inhibition in mm for each antibiotic and antiseptic as shown in Diagram 3. Record on your Lab Data Sheet in Table 1 <u>and on the board.</u>

15. Find the class average ring of inhibition in mm for antibiotics and antiseptics and record in Table 2.

16. Rank order the antibiotics and antiseptics from best--> worst.

17. Make a bar graph and divide it into 2 sections, one depicting antibiotic results and one antiseptic results.

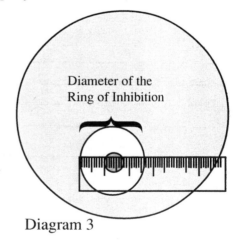
Diameter of the Ring of Inhibition

Diagram 3

18. Which antibiotic was most effective against the bacteria? the least effective? How do you know?

19. Which antiseptic was most effective against the bacteria? the least effective? How do you know?

20. Why was a control used in this experiment?

21. Is the size of the zone of inhibition on a plate necessarily a criterion for the effectiveness of an antibiotic in a human being? Why or why not?

22. Why might antibiotics differ in their effectiveness against *E. Coli?*

The Effectiveness of Antibiotics and Antiseptics *Laboratory Data Sheet*

Prelab

1. _____

2. _____

3. _____

4. _____

Laboratory

5. _____   6. _____   7. _____   8. _____   9. _____   10. _____   11. _____   12. _____   13. _____

Analysis--- Day 3

14. _____

Table 1.

Antibiotic	Ring of Inhibition (mm)	Antiseptic	Ring of Inhibition (mm)
Control		Control	

15. _____

Table 2. (Class Average)

Antibiotic	Avg. Ring of Inhibition (mm)	Antiseptic	Avg. Ring of Inhibition (mm)
Control		Control	

16. Antibiotics =_____

    Antiseptics=_____

17. _____ See graph below.

18. _____

    _____

19. _____

    _____

20. _____

    _____

21. _____

    _____

22. _____

    _____

17.

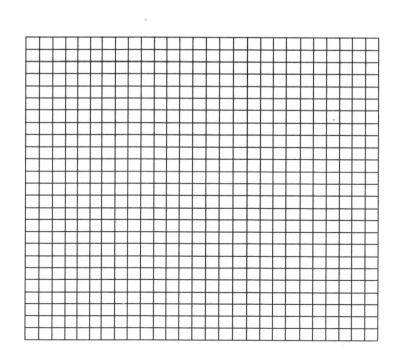

Serial Dilutions

Prelab

In the environment of a favorable closed system, a single yeast can multiply to millions of cells overnight. The growth curve of yeasts in this system shows several important features. After the yeasts are first introduced into the system a period of slow growth occurs, followed by a period of exponential growth. A period of stasis then occurs, culminating in the decline of the population as food is consumed and waste products accumulate.

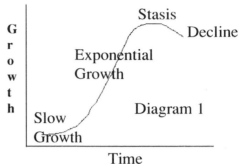

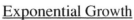
Exponential Growth

During the period of rapid growth, the yeasts reproduce at an exponential rate. Their growth can be described mathematically as $Y = a(C)^x$, where:

a= initial starting number
C= change factor
x= number of time the change occurs

> Example: Starting with a single yeast cell, how many yeast cells would there be after 30 generations?
> a= 1 ; C= 2 (population doubles when every cell has divided.) x= 30 (number of generations)
> Number of Yeasts = $1 (2)^{30} =$ 1.07×10^9

Diluting Large Populations

Since large populations of yeasts are produced in a short time through exponential growth, it is necessary to devise a way to reduce their number, but still be able to count them accurately. One such method is called **serial dilutions--** an specific amount of medium containing yeasts is diluted by precise amounts until a countable number of yeasts is obtained.

Example--Yeasts are grown overnight in a test tube. The original population is diluted by 10^{-2}, then plated. 120 yeast colonies are then counted. What was the original concentration of yeasts?

The original population and .1 dilution produce uncountable numbers (lawn). The .01 dilution gives 120 yeast colonies/mL.(Diag.2)

$120 \times 10^2 = 12,000$

The original concentration= 12,000 yeasts/mL

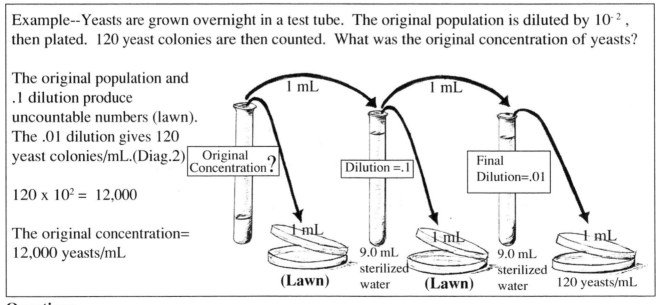

Questions

1. Describe the growth of yeast in a favorable closed environment.
2. Do the problems concerning exponential growth on your Lab Data Sheet.
3. Why must yeast be diluted before being spread onto agar?
4-5. Do the dilution problems on your Lab Data Sheet.

Laboratory- Which Type of Sugar grows Baker's Yeast most Effectively?

Materials
Per group: 3 nutrient agar petri dishes (plates), 2 sterile dilution tubes with 9.0 mL sterile water, 1 sterile test tube, test tube rack. Bunsen Burner, glass spreader, alcohol, plating wheel, .1 mL pipettes and sterile tips or sterile plastic pipettes. For the class: 1% concentrations of the following sugars containing Baker's yeast: glucose, sucrose, fructose, maltose ; optional: vortex mixer.

Procedure   *Your teacher will assign each group a type of sugar.*
6. Label 3 nutrient agar plates with the name of your sugar. Label the first "no dilution," the second ".1," and the third ".01."
7. Obtain a 3 mL sample of yeast in your assigned sugar in a sterile test tube. Swirl or vortex the sample completely.
   - a) Dip the glass spreader into alcohol and immediately
     move it through a flame.   Diagram 3
   - b) Let the alcohol flame go out.
   - c) Open a nutrient agar plate 2-3 cm and touch the glass spreader
     to the agar where there are no yeast to let it cool.
   - d) Using a sterile pipette, remove 1 mL from the sample tube, place
     it on the petri dish labeled "no dilution," and spread. (Diagram 3)
   - e) Move the top of the plating wheel in a circle and move the
     glass spreader through yeast it a back and forth motion 5-6 times.
8. Remove another 1 mL sample using sterile technique and place it in the first dilution tube. Swirl or vortex the first dilution tube completely. Using a sterile pipette, remove 1 mL from the dilution tube, plate it on the petri dish labeled ".1,"(Diag. 4)
9. After swirling or vortexing the first dilution tube, remove 1 mL and put it into the second dilution tube. Swirl or vortex this second and final dilution tube completely. Remove a 1 mL sample and plate it using sterile technique onto the agar petri dish labeled ".01."
10. Place the plates up side down in an incubato at 37 °C. Check them after 48 hours.

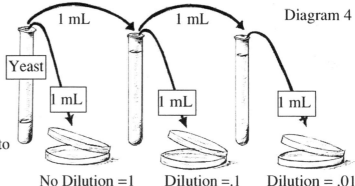

No Dilution =1   Dilution =.1   Dilution = .01

After 48 Hours
11. Without opening the plate, count the number of colonies which grew on each of your plates and record the number in your lab notebook in Table 1. (Uncountable = lawn)
12. Which of the test tubes provided a countable sample?
13. Using the countable sample, calculate the concentration of yeast/mL for your sugar and write it in Table 1 and on the board.
14. Record the average yeast concentrations of the other groups' sugars and record them in Table 2.

Analysis
15. Graphing: Make a bar graph of the avg. yeast concentration vs. sugar type in your lab notebook.
16. List in rank order the best ----> worst sugar for growing yeast.
17. Diagram and describe how serial dilutions allow large populations to be counted.

106

Serial Dilutions

Prelab

1. _____

2a. Using the formula $Y = a(C)^x$, fill in the table.
   Graph 10 generations of yeast growth.

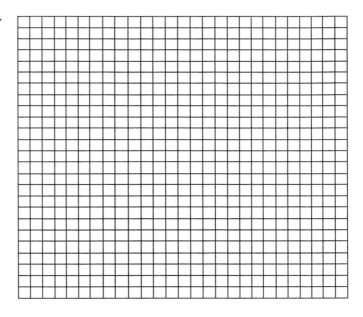

Generation	Number of Yeasts
1	2
2	
3	
4	
5	
6	
7	
8	
9	
10	

2b. Describe the graph line._____

2c. What is this type of growth called? _____

3. _____

4. A researcher grows yeast overnight, then takes a sample. After diluting the sample by 10^{-4}
   and plating, she counts 225 yeast cells. What was the original concentration of the yeast?

5. A researcher believes he has 30,000 yeast cells/mL in his concentration. Diagram and describe
   how he would dilute the sample to achieve a countable number (50-500) of yeast on a petri dish.

Laboratory- Which Type of Sugar grows Baker's Yeast most Effectively?

6. _____ 7. _____ 8. _____ 9. _____ 10. _____ 11. _____

12. _____ 13. _____ 14. _____

Table 1.   Sugar=_____

Dilution	# of Colonies	Yeast/ mL
0		
10^{-1}		
10^{-2}		

Table 2.   Class Data

Sugar	Avg. Conc.

Analysis

15. _____

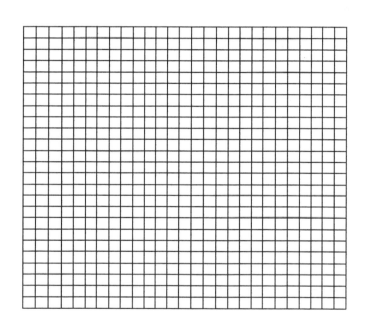

16. _____

17.

Fibonacci Sequences

Prelab

Leonardo Fibonacci was an Italian mathematician who discovered a sequence of numbers which describes many patterns found in nature. The Fibonacci Sequence is an excellent example of how mathematics can be used to describe natural patterns.

In his book *Liber abaci*, published in 1202, Fibonacci postulated his well known rabbit reproduction problem.

Start with a pair of rabbits--one male and one female born on January 1. Work with the following assumptions:

1. All months are of equal length.
2. At the age of two months, each pair produces a male and female offspring, and then another mixed pair each month thereafter.
3. No rabbit dies during the year.

Fibonacci wanted to know how many pairs of rabbits there would be after one year.

Study the diagram showing the first half year below.   (Diagram 1)

Month	Pairs of Rabbits	No. of Pairs
Jan. 1		1
Feb. 1		1
Mar. 1		2
Apr. 1		3
May 1		5
June 1		8

Questions

1. Study the sequence of numbers in column labeled ' Number of Pairs.' How many pairs of rabbits will there be on July 1?

2. Complete the Fibonacci sequence for one year on your Laboratory Data Sheet.

3. How many pairs of rabbits will there be after one year?

4. If a and b represent two consecutive numbers in a Fibonacci sequence explain how you find the next number in a Fibonacci sequence.

Laboratory- Discovering Fibonacci Sequences in Nature

Materials
Pineapple, <u>closed</u> pinecone, artichoke, pencil or pen

Procedure

<u>For Pineapples and Pine Cones:</u>

Diag. 2

Steep   Medium   Gradual

5. Count the number of bracts (individual units) from the bottom to the top of pineapple <u>and</u> pinecone using the steep, medium, and gradual inclinations. (Diag. 2)

6. Record the numbers on your Laboratory Data Sheet in rank order.

<u>For Artichokes:</u>

Diagram 3

7. Count the number of leaves from the bottom to the top of the artichoke using the steep and gradual inclinations. (Diag. 3)

8. Record the numbers on your Laboratory Data Sheet in rank order.

Analysis

9. Did the numbers from the pineapple and pine cone represent Fibonacci sequences? How do you know?

10. Did the numbers from the artichoke represent Fibonacci sequences? How do you know?

11. What is a Fibonacci sequence and how is it determined?

Fibonacci Sequences

Prelab

1. _____

2.

Month	Number of Rabbit Pairs
July	
August	
September	
October	
November	
December	

3. _____

4. _____

_____

_____

Laboratory- Discovering Fibonacci Sequences in Nature

Table 1.

	Number of Units		
	Steep	Medium	Gradual
Pineapple			
Pinecone			
Artichoke		✕	

5. _____

6. _____

7. _____

8. _____

Analysis

9. _____

_____

10. _____

_____

11. _____

_____

_____

Percentage of O$_2$ in the Atmosphere

Prelab

The atmosphere is composed of many different gases, but only two--oxygen and nitrogen--make up 99% of the atmosphere. An oxygen atom consists of 8 protons, 8 neutrons, and 8 electrons. In the atmosphere it exists as the molecule O$_2$--two atoms of oxygen bonded to each other. Abundant oxygen has not always been present in the Earth's atmosphere. Through millions of years, plants and cyanobacteria have produced oxygen as a by-product of photosynthesis. Carbon dioxide, neon, argon, and other gases comprise the other final percent. Living things depend on the oxygen and carbon dioxide in the air. While plants go through photosynthesis, both animals and plants use cell respiration to produce energy.

Photosynthesis
$6CO_2 + 6H_2O \xrightarrow[\text{Chloroplasts}]{\text{Light and}} C_6H_{12}O_6 + 6O_2$

Respiration
$C_6H_{12}O_6 + 6O_2 \longrightarrow 6CO_2 + 6H_2O + \text{energy (ATP)}$

Germinating seeds do not photosynthesize since they have no leaves. Still, cell processes are occurring rapidly as the seeds use respiration--and with it oxygen-- to convert their stored food into energy to grow roots and leaves.

Questions

Diag. 1

1. Which two gases make up 99% of the atmosphere?
2. Describe an atom and a molecule of oxygen.
3. How did oxygen come into the atmosphere?
4. Which cell process is used by both animals and plants?
5. Write the equations for photosynthesis and respiration.
6. What do you notice about the equations?
7. Do seeds photosynthesize as they germinate? Why or why not?
8. Which gas do seeds utilize as they germinate? Why?

Laboratory- Determining the Percentage of Oxygen in the Atmosphere

Materials

Per group-- 10 soaked pea seeds, 10 dry pea seeds, absorbent cotton, non-absorbent cotton, **goggles,** 15% KOH in a dropping bottle, thin test tube, 2 250 mL beakers, ruler, waterproof marking pen, **gloves**

Non-absorbent
Cotton

Procedure

9. Stuff a small piece of absorbent cotton into the bottom of the test tube. (Diag. 1)

10. Put on **goggles and gloves**. Use a pipette to drip 15% KOH onto the cotton until it is soaked. Do not to touch the test tube sides with KOH.
    KOH is used to soak up carbon dioxide.

11. Stuff a piece of non-absorbent cotton over the KOH soaked cotton.

12. Place 10 soaked pea seeds on the nonabsorbent cotton and cover with another layer of non- absorbent cotton.

Pea Seeds

Non-absorbent
Cotton

Absorbent Cotton
+ KOH

13. Fill the beaker to the 125 mL mark with water.

14. Fill the test tube 1/2 way with water and invert it quickly into the beaker. (Diag. 2)

15. Add water to the beaker until the water level inside matches the water level in the test tube. *The water levels in the test tube and in the beaker must be the same!*

16. Mark the water level on the test tube with a marker.

17. Measure the distance in cm from the top of the test tube to the water line in the test tube and record this number in Table 1.

18. Follow steps 9-17 to set up a control using dry seeds.

Diag. 2

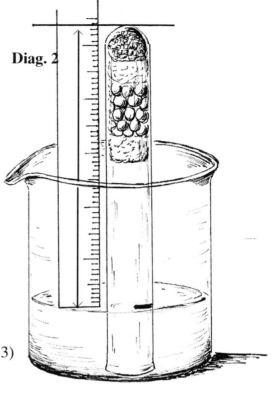

After 48 Hours   After 48 Hours   After 48 Hours

19. Measure the distance in cm from the new water line in the test tube to the original water line. Record the experimental in Table 1 and control in Table 2. (Diag. 3)

20. Calculate the percentage of oxygen in the air.

$$\frac{\text{Day 2 distance (cm)}}{\text{Original distance (cm)}} \times 100 = \% \text{ Oxygen}$$

21. Record the percentage of oxygen on your Lab Data Sheet and on the board.

Diag. 3

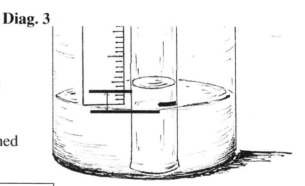

22. Calculate the class average % of oxygen and record.

23. Calculate the percentage error in this experiment for the class average and record. The % error is calculated by comparing the established values to the experimental values obtained in an experiment. Look up the established percentage of oxygen in the atmosphere.

Method to calculate percentage error:

$$\frac{|\text{Established Value} - \text{Class Average \%}|}{\text{Established Value}} = \% \text{ error}$$

Analysis

24. What % of oxygen did you determine?

25. What average % of oxygen did the class get?

26. Describe what happened in the control test tube. What was the purpose of the control?

27. What can account for the difference between the established O_2 % and the experimental O_2%?

Percentage of O$_2$ in the Atmosphere *Laboratory Data Sheet*

Prelab

1. _____;_____

2. _____

_____

3. _____

4. _____

5. _____

_____

_____

6. _____

7. _____;_____

8. _____;_____

Laboratory- Determining the Percentage of Oxygen in the Atmosphere

9. _____ 10. _____ 11. _____ 12. _____ 13. _____ 14. _____ 15. _____

16. _____

17. _____

18. _____

19. _____

20. _____

21. _____

22. _____

23. _____

Table 1. Experimental

Day 1 Distance (cm)	Day 2 Distance (cm)	% of Oxygen

Table 2. Control

Day 1 Distance (cm)	Day 2 Distance (cm)	% of Oxygen

Analysis

24. _____

25. _____

26. _____

_____

27. _____

_____

_____

Calculations:

The Ribbon of Life

Introduction

The history of life stretches back at least 3.5 billion of the Earth's 4.6 billion years. These first organisms were similar to the prokaryotic archaebacteria which inhabit the Earth today. Approximately 1.5 billion years ago the first eukaryotic cells evolved, with metazoans arising 900 million years later. Chordates and vertebrates did not appear on the scene until approximately 570 million years ago. At this time the evolutionary equivalent of the Big Bang took place; every modern phylum except one appeared in the space of 10-20 million years--the blink of an eye in geological terms. Since then, there have been alternating blossoms of life and at least five mass extinctions during which more than 50% of all species died out. The best known extinction marked the end of the Cretaceous and beginning of the Tertiary--the so-called K-T boundary--65 million years ago. There is evidence to support the idea that a large meteor or comet hit the Earth at this time which caused the extinction of thousands of species, including all of the dinosaurs.

Questions

1. When did the first organisms appear on the earth, and what where they?
2. How much time elapsed between the metazoans and the chordates?
3. When did almost all modern phyla appear?
4. How many mass extinctions have taken place in the last 570 million years?

Activity- A Mathematical Ribbon of Life

Materials

String, butcher paper, coloring pencils or pens, tape, masking tape, scissors, yarn, glue (or gluesticks), drawing paper, textbook and/or reference books.

Procedure

5. Use a scale of 100 million years = .5 m to represent the existence of the earth. Calculate the length of the timeline to represent the entire history of earth and write it on your Lab Data Sheet.

6. Until the Cambrian explosion of life took place around 600 million years ago, there was not a great diversity of life on earth. Using the scale above, calculate how long a piece of string would have to be to represent 3.9 billion years. Write it on your Lab Data Sheet.

7. Calculate the length a piece of butcher paper would have to be to represent 600 million years and write it on your LDS.

8. Have one student cut a piece of string to the length indicated in number 6.

9. Have two students cut a piece of butcher paper to the size indicated in number 7. Starting at the 600 million year mark, cut angles into the butcher paper as shown below.

10. Attach the string to the paper with tape as shown in Diagram 1.

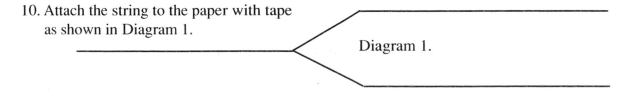

Diagram 1.

11. Mark the string every 1 billion years with a piece of masking tape attached to the string.

12. Mark the butcher paper every 100 million years, starting at the apex.

13. Mark and label the four major eras. The string represents the Precambrian. Use different colored pens to mark the Paleozoic, Mesozoic, and Cenozoic on the butcher paper.

14. Your teacher will assign you to the Precambrian era or one of 11 major time periods.

a. For the Precambrian research the following:
1. Origin of the Earth
2. Origin of prokaryotic cells (first life).
3. Oxygen rich atmosphere.
4. Origin of eukaryotic cells.
5. Origin of metazoans (multicellular organisms).

b. Make a tag for each event and hang it by yarn from the string at the appropriate place.

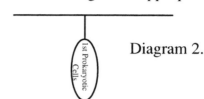

Diagram 2.

15a. Using the correct scale, mark the beginning and end of your time period.

b. For the time periods research when:
1. land plants appeared.
2. chordates appeared.
3. fish appeared.
4. amphibians appeared.
5. reptiles appeared.
6. birds appeared.
7. mammals appeared.
8. land plants appeared.
9. flowering plants appeared.
10. human beings appeared.

The Time Periods:
Quaternary
Tertiary
Cretaceous
Jurassic
Triassic
Permean
Carboniferous
Devonian
Siliurian
Ordovician
Cambrian

c. On a separate piece of paper, draw and label 8-10 representative plants and animals of your time period. Cut them out and place them in the appropriate time period along with a label giving the name and one or two facts about the organism.

Diagram 3.

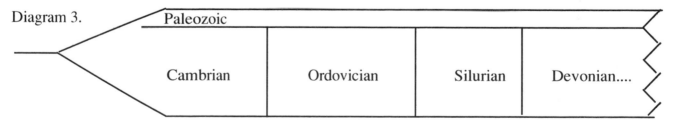

Analysis

16. For what *percentage* of the entire history of earth was there no life? has there been life?

17. How long after the origin of earth did it take for prokaryotic cells to originate? for oxygen to accumulate? Why?

18. How long did it take from the first prokaryotic organism until eukaryotic organisms originated?

19. How long did it take from the first eukaryotes until the first metazoans?

20a. When did chordates appear? b. the first fish? c. the first amphibians? d. the first reptiles? e. the first birds? f. the first mammals? g. the first plants on land? h. the first flowering plants?

21. How long did dinosaurs rule the earth? For what percentage of the total earth's history? How long have they been extinct?

22. When did the first human beings appear? For what *percentage* of earth's history have human beings been here?

The Ribbon of Life

Introduction

1. _____

2. _____

3. _____

4. _____

Activity- A Mathematical Ribbon of Life

5. _____

6. _____

7. _____

8. _____

9. _____

10. _____

11. _____

12. _____

13. _____

14a. _____ b. _____

15a. _____ b. _____ c. _____

Analysis

16. _____;_____

17. _____;_____ ; _____

_____

18. _____

19. _____

20a. _____ b. _____ c. _____

  d. _____ e. _____ f. _____

  g. _____ h. _____

21. _____ ; _____ ; _____

_____

22. _____ ; _____

Stimuli, Senses, and Time of Response

Prelab

<u>Senses:</u>

Senses such as touch, sight, and hearing are used to perceive the environment. After the information has been received, it is processed by the brain, which then acts upon the information by sending a nerve impulse to the proper body area--a stimulus produces a response. Typically, organisms can respond in only two ways to environmental stimuli—quickly by contracting muscles, or slowly by secreting substances such as hormones.

Regardless of the type of stimulus—light, heat, sound, taste, touch— the type of electrochemical impulse propagated along the nerves is the same. Perception is achieved when different areas of the brain are stimulated. The degree of stimulation is determined by the number of neurons going beyond the threshold level to send an impulse.

<u>Gravity</u>

Gravity can be used to help measure the speed of response of the senses. All objects accelerate uniformly toward earth regardless of their mass. Since the acceleration of gravity is known—9.8 m/sec²—and the distance an object falls can be measured, the time can be precisely calculated.

Example: An object falls a distance of 75 cm. How many seconds did it fall?

$$t = \sqrt{\frac{2d}{g}}$$

t= time (sec)
d= distance (m)
g= 9.8 m/sec²

① $t = \sqrt{\dfrac{2\,(75\ cm)}{9.8\ m/sec^2}}$

② Convert cm —> m
75cm = .75m

③ $t = \sqrt{\dfrac{1.5\ m}{9.8\ m/sec^2}}$

④ $t = \sqrt{.15\ sec^2}$

⑤ $t = .39\ sec$

Through a distance of 75 cm, the object was in the air .39 seconds.

Questions

1. Name three senses.

2. How can the body react to environmental stimuli?

3. What can be stated about the types of electrochemical impulses?

4. How is perception achieved, and what determines the degree of stimulation?

5. What is the formula to determine the time of fall of an object?

6. Do the problems on your Lab Data Sheet.

7. Write a hypothesis for the Laboratory. Predict the rank order of response time to light, sound, and touch stimuli and write it on your Lab Data Sheet.

Laboratory- **Which Stimulus Causes the Fastest Response Time?**

Materials

Meter Stick, stack of paper towels, blindfold, calculator

Procedure

Sight Stimulus

8. Work in groups of two.

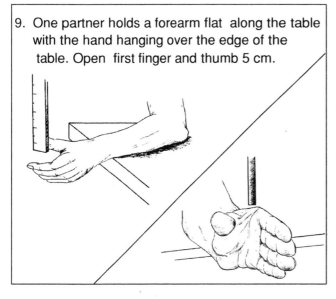

9. One partner holds a forearm flat along the table with the hand hanging over the edge of the table. Open first finger and thumb 5 cm.

10. Place a stack of paper towels on the floor beneath your partner's hand to cushion the meter stick if it is not caught.

11. Hold the meter stick with the O (zero) end directly above the opened fingers.

12. Release the meter stick and have your partner catch it as soon as it falls. Record the number <u>above the finger</u> in Table 1 on the Lab Data Sheet (LDS).

13. Do this procedure ten times. Record the distances on your Lab Data Sheet in Table 1.

Sound Stimulus

14. Blindfold <u>the same person</u> who did the sight stimulus.

15. Repeat steps 9-12. This time the partner releasing the meter stick will say "now" as the meter stick is released.

16. Repeat nine more times and record the data in Table 1 on your Lab Data Sheet.

Touch Stimulus

17. Keep the same person blindfolded. Repeat steps 8-12. This time touch your partner on the hand <u>not catching the meter stick</u> exactly as the meter stick is released.

18. Repeat nine more times and record the data in Table 1 on your Lab Data Sheet.

Analysis

19. Find the average distance for each type of stimulus and record in Table 1 on your LDS.

20. Based on the average distances, calculate the average fall times using the formula $t = \sqrt{\dfrac{2d}{g}}$ and record in Table 1 in your lab notebook.

21. Make a bar graph of the average fall times vs. the types of stimuli.

22. From your graph rank order the actual times of response to the various stimuli. Was your hypothesis correct? Why do you think the order came out this way?

Stimuli, Senses, and Time of Response *Laboratory Data Sheet*

Prelab

1. _____

2. _____

3. _____

4. _____

5. _____

6. a. An object falls 25 cm. How many seconds did it fall?

   b. An object falls .65 m. How many seconds did it fall?

   c. An object falls 212 cm. How many seconds did it fall?

7. _____

_____

Laboratory- Which Stimulus Causes the Fastest Response Time?

Table 1.

Trial	Distance of Fall(cm)		
	Sight	Sound	Touch
1			
2			
3			
4			
5			
6			
7			
8			
9			
10			

8. _____ 9. _____

10. _____ 11. _____

12. _____ 13. _____

14. _____ 15. _____

16. _____ 17. _____

18. _____

Avg. Distance= _____ _____ _____

Fall Time = _____ _____ _____

Analysis

19. _____

20. _____

21. _____

22. _____

_____

_____

_____

_____

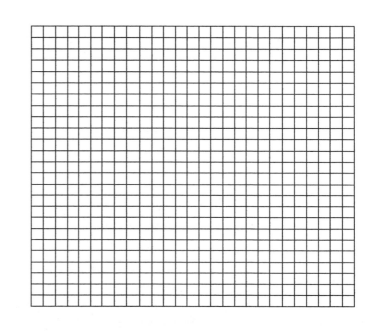

    124

Work, Power, and Calories

Prelab

Whenever a force moves an object through a distance, work is done.

$$\text{Work} = \text{Force} \times \text{Distance} \qquad \text{or} \qquad W = Fd$$

Force is measured in Newtons. Work is measured in Joules= Newton-meter
$$\text{kg} \times 9.8 = \text{Newton (N)} \quad \text{where 9.8 is the acceleration of gravity.}$$

The same amount of work is done when a object is carried up a flight of stairs, whether it takes one minute or ten minutes. Why is it that a person will be tired after running up a flight of stairs carrying an object, but will not be tired if he requires 10 minutes to carry the same object up the same flight of stairs? The answer lies in the term power. Power is used to show how fast work is being done, and is the amount of work done in a unit of time. Power is measured in watts.

$$\text{Power} = \frac{\text{Work}}{\text{Time}} = \frac{\text{Joules}}{\text{Second}} = \text{Watt}$$

Example 1:

A girl with a mass of 50 kg runs up 4.2 m of stairs in 3 seconds.
How much power in watts did she use?

Work = Force x distance

Force= 50kg x 9.8 = 490 N   Work= 490 N X 4.2 m =2058 Joules

Power= Work/ Time   =   2058 Joules / 3 seconds = 686 watts of power

However, in biology and medicine, energy measurements are commonly expressed in calories. A calorie is the amount of heat energy necessary to raise 1 g of water from 14.5 to 15.5 °C. For dietary measurements the Kilocalorie, or Kcal, is used. A Kcal is 1000 calories and is often written as Calorie.

For ease of conversion, 1.000 calorie= 4.186 J. There is no time factor involved with calories.

Example 2:

In Example 1, how many Calories (dietary measurement) did the girl use
to run up the stairs?

2058 Joules/ 4.186 = 491.6 calories   491.6/ 1000 = .4916 Cal, or approximately .5 Calorie

Questions

1. What unit is force measured in? Work?
2. What is the unit for power?
3. How is power different from work?
4. How is energy measured in biology and medicine? for diet information?
5. What is a calorie? Kcal? Calorie?
6. Do the problems on your Laboratory Data Sheet.

Laboratory- Watts, Calories, and Running up Stairs

Materials
Stairway of at least 10 steps, Meter stick, kilogram scale, stop watch, student volunteers

Procedure
7. Measure the height of one stair in meters and multiply it times the number of stairs. Record in Table 1 of your Laboratory Data Sheet.

8. Find your mass in kg and multiply it by 9.8 to find the number of Newtons. Record in Table 1.

9. Have a classmate record the amount of time it takes you to run up the stairs.

10. Calculate the power it took for you to run up the stairs.

> Method:
> $$\text{Power} = \text{Work}/\text{Time} == \frac{\text{Force(N)} \ X \ \text{Distance(m)}}{\text{Time (sec)}}$$

11. Calculate the number of Calories it took to run up the stairs and record it on your Lab Data Sheet and the board.

> Method:
> $$\text{Joules} = \text{Force} \ x \ \text{distance}$$
> $$\text{Calories} = \text{Joules} / 4,186$$

12. Record the power in watts and the number of Calories on your Lab Data Sheet and on the board.

Analysis
13. Find the class average of watts of power and Calories necessary to climb the stairs.

14. Make a bar graph showing the watts of power you used and the class average.

15. Could the average power used by the class to climb the stairs light a 100 W light bulb? If yes, how many?

16. Did the fastest person use the most power? Why or why not?

17. If the distance is increased, what must happen to maintain the same amount of power?

18. If the force is increased, and the distance remains the same, what must happen to the time to maintain the same amount of power?

19. A cola contains 150 Calories. Using your Calorie measurements, how many seconds would you have to run up stairs to consume 150 Calories?

Work, Power, and Calories

Prelab

1. _____;_____

2. _____

3. _____

   _____

4. _____;_____

5. _____;_____

   _____

Problems

6a. A boy with a mass of 63 kg runs up 10 m of stairs in 6.4 seconds. How much power did he use?

6b. A girl with a mass of 42 kg runs up 10 m of stairs in 5.3 seconds. How much power did she use?

6c. Calculate the number of Calories (kcals) the boy and girl used in problems 6a and 6b.

   Boy=

   _____

   Girl=

Laboratory- Watts, Calories, and Running Up Stairs

Table 1.

7. _____

Mass	X	9.8	= N

Height of 1 stair(m)	# of Stairs	Distance (m)	Time(sec)

8. _____

9. _____

10. _____

Table 2.

11. _____

Force (N)	X	Distance (m)	=Work (J)

Joules	/	sec	=Watts

12, _____

Analysis

13. Class Avg. watts = _____

     Class Avg. Calories = _____

Table 3.

Joules	÷	4,186	=	Calories
		4,186		

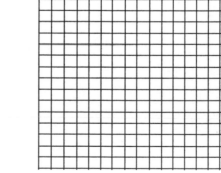

14. _____

15. _____

    _____

16. _____

    _____

17. _____

    _____

18. _____

    _____

19. _____

The Effect of UV Light on Yeast

Prelab

Ultraviolet light (UV) has a wavelength range of 400 nm to 15 nm placing it between visible light and X-Rays on the Electromagnetic Spectrum. It has a shorter wavelength and therefore more energy than visible light. (Diagram 1)

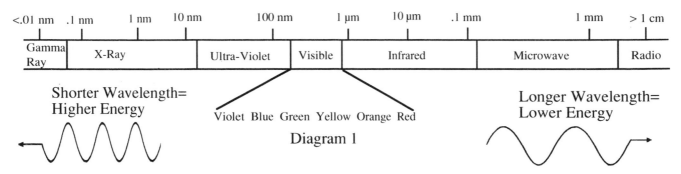

Diagram 1

UV light at a wavelength between 290 and 310 nm causes melanin production in skin cells of human beings, which causes a person's skin to become darker. This same wavelength is necessary for vitamin D production in human beings. UV is a type of nonionizing radiation which can damage cells, and overexposure to UV light in sunlight can cause sunburns which could lead to skin cancer. Thanks to the ozone layer, only a small fraction of the UV light from the sun is able to penetrate the Earth's atmosphere. Directly looking at UV light without protective eyewear can damage the retina of the eye. *Since there are no nerve cells in the retina, damage can occur with no sensation of pain.* Certain wavelengths of UV light kill cells and are used to sterilize medical instruments.

Questions
1. Where is UV light found in the Electromagnetic Spectrum?
2. What is its wavelength range?
3. Is UV more or less energetic than visible light? Why?
4. Which wavelength causes suntans and sunburns?
5. What can these lead to?
6. How much of the UV from the sun penetrates the Earth's atmosphere?
7. Why is it necessary to wear protective eyewear when working with UV light?
8. Why can UV light be used to sterilize medical instruments?

Laboratory- The Effect of UV Light on Yeast

Materials
Per group: 2 UV sensitive liquid yeast cultures in petri dishes, UV lamp, **goggles**, 10 nutrient agar petri dishes, glass spreader, plating wheel, Bunsen burner or alcohol lamp, striker, 2 pipetters with sterile tips (or 10 sterile plastic pipettes), latex gloves, sterile cover dish, watch measuring in seconds
Caution: Make sure your protective eyewear does not allow UV light to pass through. Sterile *technique must be used throughout the lab to ensure the proper results.*

Procedure
9. Label 5 nutrient agar plates UV 0 sec, UV 15 sec, UV 30 sec, UV 45 sec, and UV 60 sec. Label 5 more agar plates Control 0 sec, Control 15 sec, Control 30 sec, Control 45 sec, and Control 60 sec.

10. Place the experimental yeast sample 10 cm under the UV lamp but do not turn it on yet!!

11. Line up both sets of labeled petri dishes in order from 0 sec --> 60 sec so that you can work quickly with them.

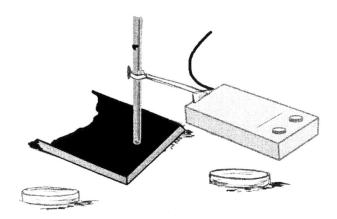

12. Raise the sterile cover and remove .1 mL of yeast from the experimental culture and .1 mL from the control culture in separate pipetters. (See Diagram 3)

13. Put the .1 mL samples onto the appropriately labeled nutrient agar plates and get new tips (or sterile plastic pipettes.)

Diagram 3

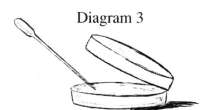

14. **Put on gloves,** turn on the UV light over the experimental culture, **and get ready to move fast!**

15. Simultaneously remove samples of yeast at 15, 30, 45, and 60 seconds from both the experimental and control plates and place onto the appropriately labeled nutrient agar plates.

16. Spread the yeast onto the plates using sterile technique (Diag. 4)
   a) Dip the glass spreader into alcohol and immediately move it through a flame.   Diagram 4
   b) Let the alcohol flame go out.
   c) Open a nutrient agar plate 2-3 cm and touch the glass spreader to the agar where there are no yeast to let it cool.
   d) Move the top of the plating wheel in a circle and move the glass spreader through yeast in a back and forth motion 5-6 times.

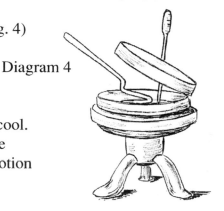

17. Store the plates up side down at 37 °C in an incubator for 48 hours.

18. **After 48 Hours**--Without opening the petri dishes, count the number of yeast colonies on each and record in Table1 on your Lab Data Sheet.

Analysis

19. Make a graph of Time vs. Yeast Colonies. Plot the control and experimental numbers on the same graph.

20. What was the reason for the control?

21. What was the effect of UV light on the yeast as time increased? Why?

The Effect of UV Light on Yeast

Laboratory Data Sheet

Prelab

1. _____

2. _____

3. _____

4. _____

5. _____

6. _____

7. _____

8. _____

Laboratory- The Effect of UV Light on Yeast

9. _____   10. _____   11. _____

12. _____   13. _____   14. _____

15. _____16. _____

17. _____

18. _____

Table 1.

	Number of Colonies				
Time(sec)	0	15	30	45	60
Control					
UV Light					

Analysis

19. _____ See Graph Below

20. _____

21. _____

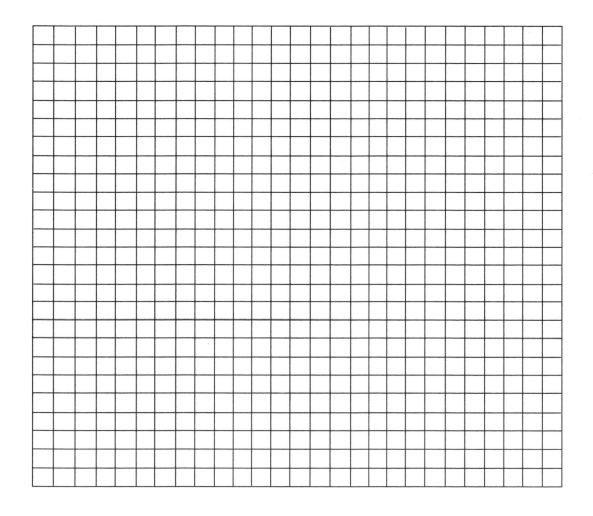

Family Genetics

Introduction

Several hundred identified traits in human beings are inherited according to Mendelian genetics. Mendelian dominant and recessive alleles must be present in pairs--one on each homologous (e.g. paternal and maternal #1) chromosome-- to produce a trait. Three combinations of pairs of alleles are then possible--homozygous dominant (PP), homozygous recessive (pp), and heterozygous (Pp).

Example

The ability to taste phenylthiocarbamide (PTC) is a well-known dominant/ recessive trait. Persons who can taste PTC have inherited at least one dominant allele (P) while non-tasters have inherited two recessive alleles (pp).   PTC taster = PP or Pp   PTC non-taster= pp

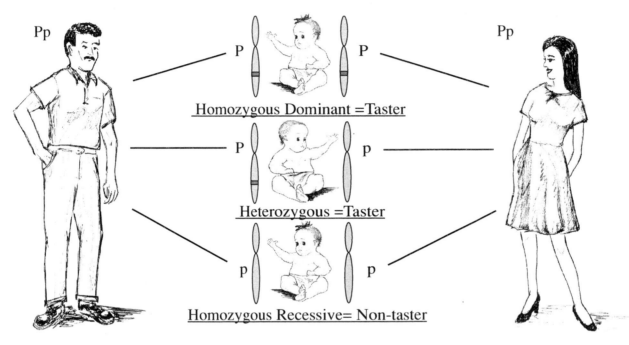

Each pair of homologous chromosomes consists of one chromosome from the mother and one from the father. In human beings the mother and father each contribute 23 chromosomes to produce the diploid number for a human baby-- 46 chromosomes in 23 pairs. A person homozygous for a trait on a chromosome (PP, for example) will contribute only one type of allele (P), while a person heterozygous for the trait (Pp) may contribute a recessive or dominant allele (P or p).

Questions

1. How many alleles does it take to make a trait in Mendelian genetics?
2. What are homologous chromosomes?
3. What are the three combinations of alleles which will produce a trait?
4. Describe the two genotypes of a PTC taster and one genotype of a PTC non-taster.
5. How many chromosomes does the mother contribute to the child? The father?
6. How many total chromosomes will a normal human being have?
7. How many types of alleles can a homozygous trait contribute to a child? A heterozygous trait?

Activity- Human Traits and Probability

Materials
One coin for mother and one coin for father, pencil or pen

Procedure
8. Following the directions below, determine which allele each parent contributes to the child for each trait.

    a. For each heterozygous trait, the recessive or dominant allele could be inherited.
       Flip a coin for each heterozygous trait to determine which trait is passed to the child.

         Heads = dominant trait   Tails = recessive trait

    b. For homozygous traits, no coin toss will be necessary since only one type of allele is produced.

    c. Fill in the children's genotypes and phenotypes in Table 1 on the Lab Data Sheet.

The designated traits on each chromosome are:

Chromosome	Trait	Chromosome	Trait
1	Rh + / Rh-	13	Normal vision= M;
2	Unattached Earlobe= U;att.= u		Retinitis Pigmentosa= m
3	Right thumb over left = R ; r	14	PTC Taster= X; non= x
4	Tongue Roller = T ; non = t	15	Z= normal teeth; z= buck teeth
5	Right Handed = H; left = h	16	W= no twinning; w= twinning
6	Interdigital Hair= I; none= i	17	Eye Color; Brown = B;
7	Normal Hair Line = P;		non-brown= b
	(Widow's Peak= p)	18	No Ear Hair= A; ear hair= a
8	Full Lips = F; thin lips = f	19	Norm.=D;Hitchhikr. Thumb=d
9	Blood type (A, B, O, AB)	20	No Dimples = Q; dimples = q
10	Concave nose = C; convex= c	21	Norm. knee= K;knob. knees=k
11	Normal melanin =Y; albinism= y	22	Norm. eye brows=E;bushy=e
12	Normal= S; Phenylketonuria=s	Sex	Sex- XX = female; XY = male

** **Note: These traits are not necessarily found on these chromosomes, nor are they necessarily strict Mendelian traits. They have been selected only as examples.**

Analysis
9. If both parents are heterozygous for a trait, what is the probability that the child would inherit the recessive trait? the dominant trait? (Hint: Use a Punnett Square.)
10. Compare your three children's genotypes. Are they the same? Why or why not?
11. Did any of your children get Retinitis Pigmentosa or Pheylketonuria? Why or why not?
12. What is the probability that two children from the same parents will receive the identical traits along <u>all 23</u> chromosomes?

Family Genetics

Introduction

1. _____

2. _____

3. _____

4. _____

5. _____

6._____

7. _____

Activity- **Human Traits and Probability**

8.   Put the **genotype** on the top line and the **phenotype** on the bottom line for each chromosome.

Table 1.

Chromosome	Mom	Dad	Child 1	Child 2	Child 3
1	Rh+/Rh-	Rh-/Rh-			
2	Uu	Uu			
3	Rr	rr			
4	tt	Tt			
5	Hh	hh			
6	ii	Ii			
7	Pp	Pp			
8	ff	FF			
9	$I^A I^B$	ii			
10	CC	cc			
11	YY	Yy			
12	Ss	SS			
13	Mm	MM			

Chromosome	Mom	Dad	Child 1	Child 2	Child 3
14	Xx	Xx			
15	Zz	zz			
16	ww	Ww			
17	Bb	BB			
18	aa	aa			
19	Dd	Dd			
20	qq	Qq			
21	Kk	Kk			
22	Ee	ee			
Sex	XX	XY			

Analysis

9. _____;_____

10. _____

_____

11. _____

_____

12._____

Crossing Over and Gene Mapping

Introduction

While working with peas, Mendel happened to pick seven different traits each of which resided on a different one of the seven chromosomes of peas. These genes assorted independently because they were on different chromosomes. When Mendel studied two traits at the same time, ie, tall and yellow pod color, he obtained a 9:3:3:1 ratio in the F_2 generation. However, early in the 20th century, researchers working on dihybrid crosses started obtaining results different from 9:3:3:1. They reasoned that the two genes they were studying were located on the same chromosome. Two genes located on the same chromosome are now known as **linked genes**.

Example: In the *Drosophila* fruit fly, the dominant alleles for Gray body (G) and Long wings (L); both reside on chromosome #2. The recessive alleles are black body (g) and short wings (l). A male fly homozygous for gray body and long wings (GGLL) is crossed with a female homozygous for black body and short wings (ggll). What are the expected results in the F_1 and F_2 generations?

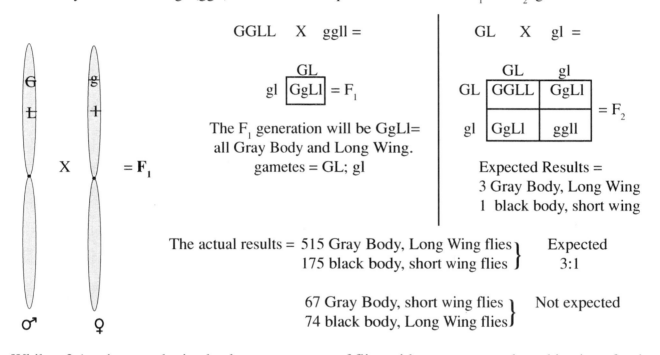

GGLL X ggll =

$$\frac{GL}{gl \boxed{GgLl}} = F_1$$

The F_1 generation will be GgLl=
all Gray Body and Long Wing.
gametes = GL; gl

X   = **F₁**

GL X gl =

	GL	gl
GL	GGLL	GgLl
gl	GgLl	ggll

$= F_2$

Expected Results =
3 Gray Body, Long Wing
1 black body, short wing

The actual results = 515 Gray Body, Long Wing flies } Expected
175 black body, short wing flies } 3:1

67 Gray Body, short wing flies } Not expected
74 black body, Long Wing flies }

♂   ♀

While a 3:1 ratio was obtained, a large percentage of flies with an unexpected combination of traits was also consistently found. Scientists explained the unexpected flies with a phenomenon called **crossing over**. During the first meiotic prophase, similar pieces of homologous chromosomes would break off and exchange. These crossover chromosomes explained the unexpected flies.

Homologous
Chromosomes
crossing over
during prophase
of meiosis I.

Maternal # 1   Paternal #1   Crossover Event   Crossover Chromosomes

After a number of experiments, scientists realized that the frequency of crossovers between two genes on the same chromosome was directly proportional to the distance apart the two genes lay on that chromosome. The farther apart two genes are on a chromosome, the higher the crossing over frequency. The closer two genes are on a chromosome, the lower the crossing over frequency. Crossover frequencies could therefore be used to establish genetic maps.

Example:

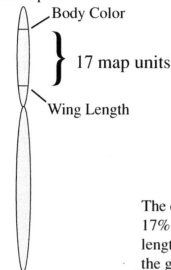

Body Color

} 17 map units

Wing Length

Chromosome #2

In the cross between Gray Body, Long Wing flies and black body short wing flies, the results were:

Gray Body, Long Wing flies = 515
black body, short wing flies = 175 } =Expected

Gray Body, short wing flies = 67
black body, Long Wing flies = 74 } = Crossovers= 141

Total flies = 831

Frequency of crossovers = 141 / 831=   17%

The crossover frequency for body color and wing length is established at 17%. Therefore the distance between the genes for body color and wing length is 17 map units. Note that this technique does not indicate *where* the genes for body color and wing length reside on the chromosome at this point, only that they are 17 map units apart.

Questions
1. When two genes segregate independently in a dihybrid cross, what is the expected ratio in the F_2 generation?
2. When researchers started getting results different from the expected ratio for <u>dihybrid crosses,</u> how did they explain the anomalous results?
3. When scientists started getting unexpected results for <u>linked genes</u>, how did they explain the anomalous results?
4. Diagram and describe what happens during a crossover event.
5. How can crossover frequencies be used to make a map of a chromosome?

Activity- Mapping the Genes of *Drosophila*

Materials
Paper, pencil, calculator

6. Using the crossover frequency data on your Lab Data Sheets, map three genes on three chromosomes of *Drosophilia*. (Chromosome #4 is extremely small and will not be used.)

Analysis
7. What are the strengths of this gene mapping technique? the limitations?

8. Could this technique be used to map human genes? Why or why not?

Crossing Over and Gene Mapping *Laboratory Data Sheet*

Prelab

1. _____

2._____

_____

3._____

_____

4.

5._____

_____

_____

Activity- Mapping Genes on *Drosophila* Chromosomes

6. Calculate the crossover frequency of each of the following genes and construct a gene map for each chromosome. Indicate the relative distances between the genes.

__X Chromosome__   Genes = *white eye, bar eye, scalloped wings*

bar eye x *scalloped wings*	*white eye* x *scalloped wings*	*white eye* x *bar eye*
Expected= $\left\{\begin{array}{l}205\\70\end{array}\right.$	Expected= $\left\{\begin{array}{l}142\\47\end{array}\right.$	Expected= $\left\{\begin{array}{l}301\\108\end{array}\right.$
Crossovers = $\left\{\begin{array}{l}5\\3\end{array}\right.$	Crossovers = $\left\{\begin{array}{l}42\\47\end{array}\right.$	Crossovers = $\left\{\begin{array}{l}105\\111\end{array}\right.$
c/o frequency= _____	c/o frequency= _____	c/o frequency=____

Chromosome 2 *vestigial, lobe eye, brown eye*

vestigial x *lobe eye*	*lobe eye* x *brown eye*	*vestigial* x *brown eye*
Expected= $\left\{ \begin{array}{l} 236 \\ 76 \end{array} \right.$	Expected= $\left\{ \begin{array}{l} 187 \\ 62 \end{array} \right.$	Expected= $\left\{ \begin{array}{l} 280 \\ 87 \end{array} \right.$
Crossovers= $\left\{ \begin{array}{l} 10 \\ 11 \end{array} \right.$	Crossovers= $\left\{ \begin{array}{l} 35 \\ 44 \end{array} \right.$	Crossovers= $\left\{ \begin{array}{l} 74 \\ 83 \end{array} \right.$
c/o frequency=_____	c/o frequency=_____	c/o frequency=____

Chromosome 3 *stubble bristles, spineless bristles, ebony body*

stubble x *spineless*	*stubble* x *ebony*	*spineless* x *ebony*
Expected= $\left\{ \begin{array}{l} 182 \\ 67 \end{array} \right.$	Expected= $\left\{ \begin{array}{l} 96 \\ 30 \end{array} \right.$	Expected= $\left\{ \begin{array}{l} 214 \\ 69 \end{array} \right.$
Crossovers= $\left\{ \begin{array}{l} 1 \\ 2 \end{array} \right.$	Crossovers= $\left\{ \begin{array}{l} 5 \\ 5 \end{array} \right.$	Crossovers= $\left\{ \begin{array}{l} 12 \\ 6 \end{array} \right.$
c/o frequency=_____	c/o frequency=_____	c/o frequency=____

> **Put all genes above or below the centromere.**

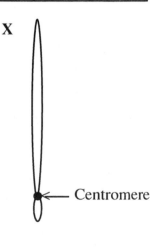

X

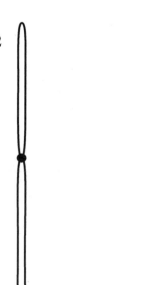

2

3

←— Centromere

Analysis

7. _____

_____

8. _____

  140

The Hardy-Weinberg Equation

Prelab

The Hardy-Weinberg Equation

The frequency of homozygous and heterozygous genotypes in a population can be calculated using the Hardy-Weinberg Equation. Information from the Hardy-Weinberg Equation can be used to determine the 'genetic health' of a population or to calculate the risk of carrying a genetic disorder.

In order to use the equation, only one piece of information has to be known--the frequency of homozygous recessives. Recessive traits require two recessive alleles to be present for the phenotype to be expressed. Their frequency in a population can be directly calculated from observation since the genotype is known from the phenotype.

Example: Attached and Unattached earlobes in human beings

In human beings, unattached earlobes (U) is dominant to attached (u) earlobes. A person will have the phenotype of attached earlobes if and only if he has the genotype uu.

In a class of 32 students, 5 were found to have attached earlobes. What is the frequency and percentage of students with attached earlobes?

attached earlobes= uu= 5/32= .156 or 15.6% of the population

However, the frequency of heterozygote (Uu) and homozygote dominant (UU) persons with unattached earlobes cannot be directly calculated. A person with unattached earlobes could be genotype UU or Uu, and it is impossible through observation to determine if a person is heterozygous or homozygous for the trait. In this case the Hardy-Weinberg formula can be used to calculate the frequency of homozygous dominants and heterozygotes in the population.

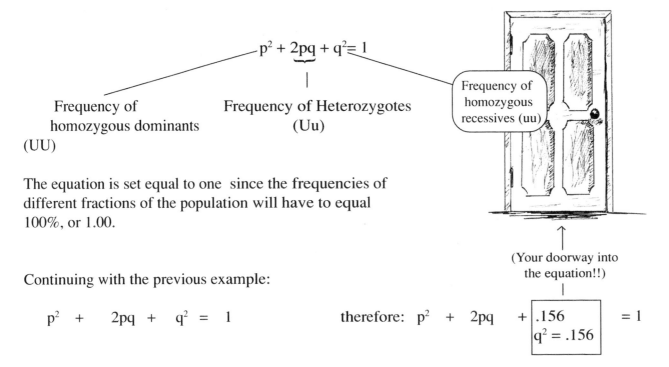

$$p^2 + 2pq + q^2 = 1$$

Frequency of homozygous dominants (UU)

Frequency of Heterozygotes (Uu)

Frequency of homozygous recessives (uu)

The equation is set equal to one since the frequencies of different fractions of the population will have to equal 100%, or 1.00.

(Your doorway into the equation!!)

Continuing with the previous example:

$$p^2 + 2pq + q^2 = 1 \qquad\qquad \text{therefore:} \quad p^2 + 2pq + \boxed{\begin{array}{l}.156 \\ q^2 = .156\end{array}} = 1$$

Copyright Spectrum Publications All Rights Reserved

Once q^2 is known, q and p can be calculated.

$$\sqrt{q^2} = q \qquad \sqrt{.156} = .39 = q$$

$$p + q = 1 \; ; \quad p = 1 - q \; ; \quad p = 1 - .39 \; ; \quad .61 = 1 - .39 \; ; \quad p = .61$$

The values for p and q can now be substituted into the equation:

$$p^2 \quad + \quad 2\,(p)\,(q) \quad + \quad q^2 \quad = \quad 1$$

$$(.61)^2 \quad + \quad 2\,(.61)(.39) \quad + \quad .156 \quad = \quad 1$$

Remember! .156 already equals q^2

$$(.37) \quad + \quad (.475) \quad + \quad .156 \quad = \quad 1$$

The Hardy-Weinberg equation is very user friendly!! If you make a mistake, the numbers will not add up to 1 (or nearly 1)!

Questions
1. What can be calculated using the Hardy-Weinberg Equation?
2. What useful information comes from the Hardy-Weinberg Equation?
3. What information must be known to use the Hardy-Weinberg Equation?
4. Explain each part of the Hardy-Weinberg Equation.
5. Why do you have to start with q^2 to calculate the other frequencies?
6. Do the problems on your Laboratory Data Sheet.

Laboratory- Calculating Genetic Frequencies of Human Traits

Materials
Pencil, paper, calculator, PTC paper

Procedure
7. Using your class as a population, calculate the frequency of homozygous recessives, heterozygotes, and homozygous dominants for the following autosomal traits: attached ear lobes, PTC taster, eye color (brown and non-brown), and handedness.
        a. Record in Table 1 on your Laboratory Data Sheet.
        b. To test PTC paper, simply place the PTC strip on your tongue.

Analysis
8. Which trait had the highest percentage of homozygous dominants? heterozygotes? homozygous recessives?

9. Why is the frequency of homozygous recessives the 'doorway' into the Hardy-Weinberg equation?

10. If a trait is 'out of Hardy-Weinberg equilibrium,' what could it mean?

The Hardy-Weinberg Equation   *Laboratory Data Sheet*

Prelab

1. _____

2. _____

3. _____

4. _____

5. _____

_____

6a. Tay-Sachs disease is an autosomal recessive trait which occurs at a frequency of 1 in 3600 in persons of Jewish ancestry. Calculate the frequency of carriers of the gene (heterozygotes) and persons who do not carry the gene (homozygous dominants). What is the probability that two heterozygotes will meet? What is the probability that they will have a child with Tay-Sachs disease?

6b. Among Caucasians, 1% of the population is homozygous recessive and 20% is heterozygous for a mutation in the CCR5 gene. Since the CCR5 gene produces a chemokine co-receptor necessary for the entry of the AIDS virus, persons with CCR5 mutations on both genes (homozygous recessives) are immune to AIDS infections. Heterozygotes can resist AIDS 2-3 years longer than normal. Calculate the percentage of Caucasians susceptible to the AIDS virus (homozygous dominants), and heterozygotes. Determine whether the Caucasian population is in Hardy-Weinberg equilibrium. If it is not, what could account for the disparity?

Laboratory- Calculating Genetic Frequencies of Human Traits

7.

Table 1.   Note: Top line= plug-in values $(.34)^2$, bottom line = frequencies $(.12)$

Trait	p^2 Homozygous Dominant	$2(pq)$ Heterozygous	q^2 Homozygous Recessive	= 1
				=_____
				=_____
				=_____
				=_____

Analysis

8. _____

_____

9. _____

_____

10. _____

_____

Probability in Biology

Introduction

Probability of a Single Event Occurring

Determining the relative frequency of a certain event or series of events occurring is called probability. Toss any unaltered coin and there is a 1 out of 2 (.5 or 50%) probability of a heads or a tails landing up. Toss any unaltered die and there is a 1 out of 6 (.16 or 16%) probability of any one number landing up. Probability is expressed as a decimal (.5) percentage (50%), or fraction (1/2). With the coin there are two choices out of a single toss, each of which has an equal probability of occurring. For the die there are six possible outcomes for each toss, each of which has an equal probability of occurring. The probability of an event occurring can be calculated with this formula:

Probability= number of events of choice   Coin= 1 = .5 or 50%   Die = 1 = .16 or 16%
 number of possible events   6

Probability of Two or More Events Occurring

How can the total probability of a separate series of events be calculated? In order to calculate the probability of 2 heads being tossed: Multiply the probability of each event occurring separately to calculate the probability of the events occurring together.

Example 1.   What is the probability of tossing two heads? Probability of tossing 1 heads = 1/2
Probability of tossing heads again = 1/2; *probability of tossing two heads in a row=1/2 x 1/2 = 1/4*

Example 2.   What is the probability of tossing 3 sixes in a row with a single die?
Probability of tossing a 6 the first time = 1/6   Probability of tossing a 6 the second time = 1/6
Probability of tossing a 6 the third time = 1/6
Probability of tossing three sixes in a row = 1/6 x 1/6 x 1/6 = 1/216

How can Probability be used in Biology?

Probability is used in genetics to make predictions (hypotheses). For example, human males produce sperm cells which can carry either an X chromosome or Y chromosome, while human females produce only X's. A Punnett Square is used to make the hypothesis.

Example 3. What is the probability of a couple having a girl or a boy as their first child?

	X	X
X	XX	XX
Y	XY	XY

Probability of having a boy the first time= 1/2
Probability of having a girl the first time= 1/2
What is the probability of a couple having three girls or three boys in a row?
1/2 x   1/2 x   1/2 =   1/8

Remember: Probability only predicts what *should* happen, not what *will* happen--especially in a small sample size. As the sample size increases, the observed probability will begin to approach the theoretical, predicted probability.

Questions

1. What is probability?
2. How is the probability of a single event occurring determined?
3. How is the probability of multiple events occurring determined?
4. Given a pair of dice, what is the probability of rolling: a. a 3 and a 4?   b. two 5's?
5. What is the probability of flipping a heads and rolling a 3 with one die?
6. What is the probability that a family could have 5 daughters? 4 sons?
7. Do the biology probability problems on the Lab Data Sheet.

Activities- Applying Probability in Biology

Activity 1-Girls and Boys

Materials

1 coin per group, paper, pencil

Procedure

8. Predict how many girls and boys will be born in 100 births and write your hypothesis in Table 1.
9. On a separate piece of paper draw a line down the center. Label one column girls and one boys.
10. Use Heads= girls and Tails = boys. Flip your coin 100 times and record each 'girl' and 'boy' in the appropriate column.
11. Record your group data in Table 1 and on the board. Calculate the class total number of girls and boys and record in Table 2.
12. Write a prediction (hypothesis) for how many girls and boys should be born according to class data and record in Table 2.

Analysis

13. Calculate the deviation from expected for group and class data.

$$\% \text{ Deviation} = \frac{|\text{girls expected - girls observed}| + |\text{boys expected - boys observed}|}{\text{Total Number of boys and girls}} \times 100$$

14. Where did the observed data match the predicted data more closely, in the group data or class data? Why?

Activity 2- Flies and Wing Length

Materials

2 coins per group, paper, pencil

Procedure

15. In Drosophila flies, long wing length is dominant (L) and vestigial is recessive (l). Two heterozygous flies (Ll) are crossed. Using a Punnett Square, calculate the probability that vestigial flies (ll) will be produced and long winged flies (LL + Ll) will be produced. Record on your Lab Data Sheet.
16. Assuming that 100 flies are born in this cross, write your hypothesis in Table 3.
17. On a separate piece of paper make 2 columns and label them LL + Ll, and ll
18. Obtain two coins. Designate heads as L and tails as l.
19. Flip the two coins together 100 times and record the results in the columns and on the board.
20. Record group data in Table 3 and class data in Table 4. Calculate the expected number of long and vestigial wing flies for class data and record in Table 4.

Analysis

21. Modify the formula in Activity 1 and calculate the deviation from expected for group and class data for Activity 2.
22. Where did the observed data match the predicted data more closely, in the group data or class data? Why?
23. Based on both activities, what can you say about sample size and probability?

Probability in Biology

Prelab

1._____

2._____

3._____

_____

4a. _____   b._____   5. _____

6._____ ; _____

7. Do your Punnett squares and calculations on a separate piece of paper.

a. Albinism is a recessive autosomal trait. A couple, both of whom are heterozygous for albinism, decide to have children. 1) What is the probability that they will have children with normally pigmented skin? _____ 2) Albinism? _____

b. In pea plants, round seed shape is dominant to wrinkled seed shape. A heterozygous round seed plant is crossed with a wrinkled seed plant.   1) What is the probability that the resulting peas will be round? _____ 2) wrinkled?_____

c. Colorblindness is a sexlinked recessive trait. A normal man marries a woman who carries the allele for colorblindness. 1) What is the probability that a daughter will be colorblind?_____ 2) a colorblind son?_____ 3) a normal son? _____

d. Unattached earlobes and Rh+ blood group are domininat traits. Attached earlobes and Rh-negative blood groups are recessive. A man heterozygous for unattached earlobes <u>and</u> Rh marries a woman who has attached earlobes and is Rh-.   What is the probability of children with unattached earlobes/Rh+?_____ unattached earlobes Rh-?_____ attached earlobes/Rh+? _____   attached earlobes/Rh-?_____

Activities- Applying Probability in Biology

<u>Activity 1</u>

8._____

9._____

10._____

11._____

12._____

Table 1.- Group Data

	Girls	Boys
Expected (hypothesis)		
Observed		

Table 2.- Class Data

	Girls	Boys
Expected (hypothesis)		
Observed		

Analysis

13.

14._____

_____

<u>Activity 2</u>

15. _____

Probability of Long Wing flies=_____

Probability of vestigial flies=_____

16. _____

17. _____

18. _____

19. _____

20. _____

Table 3.   Group Fly Data

	Long	Vestig.
Expected (hypothesis)		
Observed		

Table 4. Class Fly Data

	Long	Vestig.
Expected (hypothesis)		
Observed		

Analysis

21.

22._____

_____

23._____

_____

148

Analyzing Single Trait Crosses with χ^2

Prelab

Mendel succeeded in explaining the fundamental concepts of genetics because he used a mathematical approach to analyze his results. He recognized the 3:1 ratio in monohybrid crosses and the 9:3:3:1 ratio in dihybrid crosses. Some even question Mendel's results because they were *too good!* But how good is good? When should results be accepted as conforming to a predicted ratio, and when should they be rejected? The chi-square (χ^2) test allows you to test the **goodness of fit**: How close do the actual observed experimental data match a predicted, expected ratio in the hypothesis? The test takes into account the sample size and deviations from the expected ratio. Finally, it allows you to determine the probability that the deviation from the predicted occurred by chance alone.

Example:
   A plant breeder crosses a homozygous tall (TT) variety of pea with a short variety (tt) of pea. The tall trait is dominant to the short trait, so the breeder expects a 3:1 ratio in the F_2 generation.

   TT x tt = F_1 generation.   The F_1 are crossed = Tt x Tt

	T	T
t	Tt	Tt
t	Tt	Tt

= F_1 = Tt

	T	t
T	TT	Tt
t	Tt	tt

= F_2

Expected
Ratio = TT, Tt, Tt : tt
3 Tall : 1 short

   After the experiment is done, the breeder counts 195 tall plants and 69 short plants, for a total of 264 plants. Do these results conform to the expected 3:1 ratio?

$$\chi^2 = \frac{(O_1 - e_1)^2}{e_1} + \frac{(O_2 - e_2)^2}{e_2}$$

where   O = Observed   e= expected

Expected Tall Plants = 264 x 3/4 = 198 = 3
Expected Short Plants= 264 x 1/4 = 66 = 1

$$\chi^2 = \frac{(195-198)^2}{198} + \frac{(69 - 66)^2}{66} = .045 + .136 = .181$$

$\chi^2 = .181$ Degrees of freedom = number of data classes - 1 = 2-1 = 1
          (Data Classes= number of phenotypes in ratio= 2)

After the χ^2 and degrees of freedom have been calculated, the probability (P) value is located in a χ^2 table (Appendix 1a). A χ^2 value of .181 at one degree of freedom falls between .148 and .455 on the table, corresponding to P values of .70 and .50, respectively. This indicates there is a 50-70% probability that deviations from the expected 3:1 ratio occurred due to chance alone. The data fit the hypothesis well.
The larger the χ^2 value--and smaller the corresponding P value-- indicating large differences from the expected, the smaller the probability that the predicted ratio is correct. A different ratio might fit the data better. Typically, P values between .90 and .99 are considered strong support for a predicted ratio.

Problems
1. Do the χ^2 problems on your Lab Data Sheet.
2. On your Lab Data Sheet, formulate a hypothesis for the monohybrid corn cross.

Laboratory- Analyzing Monohybrid Corn Crosses with χ^2

Materials
per group-- Calculator, monohybrid F_2 corn, pins, paper, pencil

Procedure
3. On a separate piece of paper, make two columns stretching the entire length of the paper. Label the two columns with the classes of corn kernels.

4. Put two pins around the end of one row of kernels in the cob and read the color of the kernels to a partner. Leave one pin in the corn as a starting reference. Move the other pin around the cob one row at a time, then read the color of kernels to your partner. See Diagram 1.

Diagram 1

5. Write the results from your group in Table 1 and on the board. Write the class total results in Table 2.

Analysis
6. Using the example on the previous page, calculate the expected numbers for your group and class data and record on the Lab Data Sheet.

7. Using the example on the previous page, do the χ^2 calculations for your group and class data, and record on the Lab Data Sheet.

8. What is the probability that your predicted ratio fit the observed data for:
    a. group data?
    b. class data?

9. Can you accept your hypothesis for your class or group data? Why or why not? State in terms of probabilities.

10. Which data conform to your hypothesis more closely--the group data or class data? Why do you think this is the case?

Analyzing Single Trait Crosses with χ^2 *Laboratory Data Sheet*

Prelab

Problems

1a. In fruit flies, normal sized wings (N) are dominant to vestigial wings (n). A researcher wishes to determine which ratio the trait for normal wings exhibits in the F_2 generation. She crosses purebreeding males with normal sized wings (NN) with a vestigial females (nn). She crosses the F_1 offspring to get the F_2. She finds 437 normal winged flies and 138 vestigial flies.

    1) Show the F_1 cross.   2) Show the F_2 cross and determine the expected ratio (hypothesis).

    3) Do the χ^2 calculations for the researcher's data.   Can she accept her hypothesis? Why or why not? The χ^2 Table is in Appendix 1a.

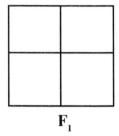
F₁

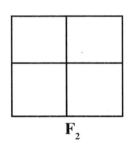
F₂

b. In pea plants, purple flowers (P) are dominant to white (p) flowers. A researcher crosses a heterozygous purple flowered plant with a white flowered plant. The results show 227 purple plants and 202 white plants. (Be careful how you calculate the expected.)

    1) Show the cross and determine the expected ratio.   2) Do the χ^2 calculations for the researcher's data. Can he accept his hypothesis? Why or why not? The χ^2 Table is in Appendix 1a.

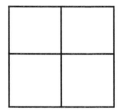

2. Formulating the Hypothesis: In this lab you will determine if the traits of purple (P) and white (p) kernel color in corn follow a Mendelian monohybrid inheritance pattern.

In the first experiment, you cross homozygous purple corn with white corn.
Write this cross using symbols: _____x_____

Diagram this cross using a Punnett
Square to get the F$_1$ generation.

What is the genotype of all offspring?

_____

F$_1$

You then crossed the F$_1$ generation to get
the F$_2$ generation. Write this cross using
symbols:

_____x_____

Diagram the above cross using a Punnett
Square to get the F$_2$ generation.
What phenotypic ratio do you get?

F$_2$

Purple = _____   White = _____

Laboratory- Analyzing Monohybrid Corn Crosses with χ^2

3._____   4._____   5._____

Analysis

6. _____

	Table 1. Group Data		Table 2. Class Data	
	Purple	White	Purple	White
Observed				
Expected				

7.

8. _____

9. _____

_____

10. _____

Analyzing 2 Trait Crosses with χ^2

Prelab

A dihybrid cross is conducted by initially crossing a homozygous dominant with a homozygous recessive. The resulting F_1 offspring are then crossed, resulting in the F_2 generation. Typically, a phenotypic ratio of 9:3:3:1 will be obtained in the F_2. The F_2 can then be analyzed using the chi square (χ^2) formula to determine how closely the experimental results conform to the expected results. The formula for χ^2 for a sample consisting of four classes, such as a 1:1:1:1 or 9:3:3:1, is:

$$\chi^2 = \frac{(O_1 - e_1)^2}{e_1} + \frac{(O_2 - e_2)^2}{e_2} + \frac{(O_3 - e_3)^2}{e_3} + \frac{(O_4 - e_4)^2}{e_4}$$

Where: O_1 = experimentally observed number for the first class
  e_1 = expected number from the first class derived from the ratio

  O_2 = experimentally observed number for the second class
  e_2 = expected number from the second class derived from the ratio

  O_3 = experimentally observed number for the third class
  e_3 = expected number from the third class derived from the ratio

  O_4 = experimentally observed number for the fourth class
  e_4 = expected number from the fourth class derived from the ratio

---

Example:

In the F_2 generation of a cross between peas with round, yellow seeds, and those with wrinkled, green seeds, Mendel obtained 315 round, yellow seeds; 108 round, green seeds; 101 wrinkled, yellow seeds; and 32 wrinkled, green seeds. Do these results conform to his prediction of a 9:3:3:1 ratio?

$$\chi^2 = \frac{(O_1 - e_1)^2}{e_1} + \frac{(O_2 - e_2)^2}{e_2} + \frac{(O_3 - e_3)^2}{e_3} + \frac{(O_4 - e_4)^2}{e_4}$$

Calculate the predicted= 315 + 108 + 101 + 32 = 556
  using the observed

556	x 9/16 = 312.75	= 9
556	x 3/16 = 104.25	= 3
556	x 3/16 = 104.25	= 3
556	x 1/16 = 34.75	= 1

$$\chi^2 = \frac{(315 - 312.75)^2}{312.75} + \frac{(108 - 104.25)^2}{104.25} + \frac{(101 - 104.25)^2}{104.25} + \frac{(32 - 34.75)^2}{34.75} = .47$$

Degrees of Freedom --> 4 - 1 = 3. At 3 degrees of freedom and a χ^2 of .47, the Probability (P) lies between .9->.99 (χ^2 chart in Appendix 1a) indicating 90-99% confidence that the data fit a 9:3:3:1 ratio. There is a 90-99% likelihood that the deviation from the expected is due to chance alone and only a 1-10% chance that another hypothesis would fit the data better. The hypothesis is accepted.

Problems

1. Do the χ^2 problems on your Lab Data Sheet.
2. Formulate a hypothesis for your corn on your Laboratory Data Sheet.

Copyright Spectrum Publications All Rights Reserved

Laboratory- Analyzing Dihybrid Corn Crosses with χ^2

Materials

per group-- Calculator, F_2 corn, pins, paper, pencil

Procedure

3. On a separate piece of paper, make four columns stretching the entire length of the paper. Label the four columns with the classes of corn kernels shown in Diagram 1.

4. Put two pins around the end of one row of kernels in the cob and read the type and color of the kernels to a partner. Leave one pin in the corn as a starting reference. Move the other pin around the cob one row at a time, reading the type and color of the kernels to your partner.

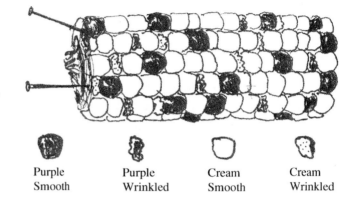

| Purple | Purple | Cream | Cream |
| Smooth | Wrinkled | Smooth | Wrinkled |

5. Write the results from your group in Table 1 and on the board. Write the class total results in Table 2.

Analysis

6. Following the example on the previous page, calculate the expected numbers for your group and class data.

7. Following the example on the first page of the lab, do the χ^2 calculations for your group and class data.

8. Can you accept your hypothesis for class or group data? Why or why not?

9. Which data conform to the 9:3:3:1 hypothesis more closely--the group data or class data? Why?

Analyzing 2 Trait Crosses with χ^2 _Laboratory Data Sheet_

Prelab

Problems

1a. A researcher expects a 1:1:1:1 ratio after doing a two trait cross with watermelons. His actual results were: 70 striped, short; 66 striped, long; 72 green, short; 73 green, long. Should he accept or reject the 1:1:1:1 hypothesis? The χ^2 table is in Appendix 1a.

b. A researcher expects a 9:3:3:1 ratio after doing a dihybrid cross with peas. Her actual results were: 152 tall, green seed; 62 tall, yellow seed; 47 short, green seed; and 19 short, yellow seed. Should she accept or reject her 9:3:3:1 hypothesis? The χ^2 table is in Appendix 1a.

2. Formulating the Hypothesis: In this lab you will determine if the traits of Purple/Cream color and Smooth/Wrinkled texture in corn follow a Mendelian dihybrid inheritance pattern. You know beforehand that Purple (P) is dominant to Cream (p) and Smooth (S) is dominant to Wrinkled (s).

In the first experiment, you cross homozygous Purple, Smooth corn with Cream, Wrinkled corn. Write this cross using symbols: _____ x _____

Diagram this cross using a Punnett Square to get the F_1 generation.

F_1

What is the genotype of all offspring?

_____

What is the phenotype of all offspring?

_____

You then crossed the F_1 generation to get the F_2 generation. Write this cross using symbols:

_____x_____

Diagram this cross using a Punnett Square to get the F_2 generation. What phenotypic ratio do you get?

Purple, Smooth= _____

Purple, Wrinkled=_____

Cream, Smooth= _____

Cream, Wrinkled=_____

F_2

Laboratory- **Analyzing Dihybrid Corn Crosses with** χ^2

3._____   4._____   5._____

Analysis

6. _____

	Table 1. Group Data			
	Purp. Sm.	Purp. Wr.	Cr. Sm.	Cr. Wr.
Observed				
Expected				

	Table 2. Class Data			
	Purp. Sm.	Purp. Wr.	Cr. Sm.	Cr. Wr.
Observed				
Expected				

7.

8. _____

9. _____

Building a Model of DNA

Introduction

The discovery of DNA's molecular structure in 1953 by James Watson and Francis Crick heralded the beginning of the now burgeoning science of molecular biology. The culmination of Watson and Crick's work was a scale model showing how the complex molecule fit together. Watson and Crick based their model on X-Ray diffraction photographs of DNA taken by Rosalind Franklin. These pictures suggested a helical structure with a width of 2 nm and repeat pattern of 3.4 nm, meaning there were 10 base pairs per complete turn of the helix.

Many characteristics of DNA will be apparent in the model--nucleotides, the double helix, antiparallel structure, 3' and 5' ends, hydrogen bonding, and adenine-thymine, guanine-cytosine base pairing. Some of these are pictured in Diagram 1.

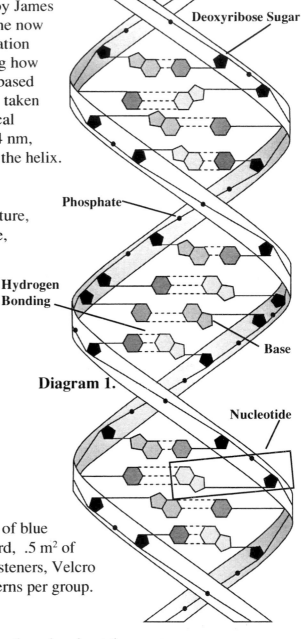

Diagram 1.

Questions
1. Who discovered the structure of DNA?
2. What did Watson and Crick build to help them understand the structure of DNA?
3. What did Watson and Crick base their model on?
4. How wide is DNA?
5. How long is the repeat pattern of DNA?
6. List 4 characteristics of DNA.

Activity- Building a Model of DNA

Materials
2 m² of black matboard, 1 m² of white matboard, .5 m² of blue matboard, .5 m² of red matboard, .5 m² yellow matboard, .5 m² of green matboard, sharp scissors, razor blades, brass fasteners, Velcro with adhesive backing, glue; 1 set of DNA model patterns per group.

Procedure
7. Trace deoxyribose sugar molecules onto the black matboard and cut them out.
8. Trace phosphate molecules onto the white matboard and cut them out.
9. Trace the base molecules onto the blue, green, yellow, and red matboards and cut them out.

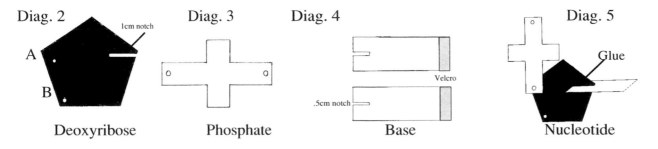

Diag. 2 — Deoxyribose
Diag. 3 — Phosphate
Diag. 4 — Base
Diag. 5 — Nucleotide

10. Punch holes as indicated in Diagram 2 at A and B. Cut a 1 cm long notch on the side opposite of A and B.

11. Punch holes in either end of the phosphate as indicated in Diagram 3.

12. Cut a .5 cm notch in the end of the bases as shown in Diagram 4.
    a. Attach a small piece of the <u>hook velcro</u> to the green (thymine) and red(guanine) bases on the side opposite the notch.
    b. Attach a small piece of the <u>fuzz velcro</u> to the blue (adenine) and yellow (cytosine) opposite the notch.

13. Making the nucleotides: Attach a phosphate to a sugar as shown in Diagram 5.
    a. Insert the notch of the base into the notch of the sugar. Glue them together.

14. Attach the nucleotides together to form a single stranded DNA.

15. Find the complementary nucleotides and join them as shown in Diagram 6.
    REMEMBER: DNA has antiparallel structure and the sugars must run in opposite directions.

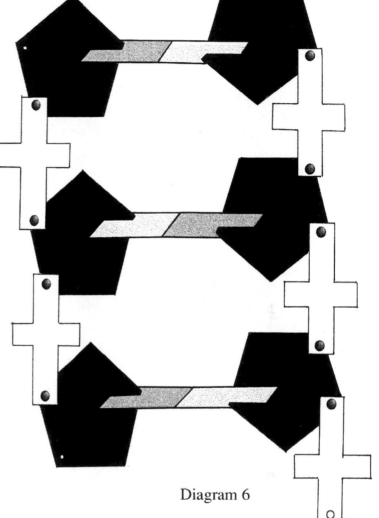

Diagram 6

16. Join your section to others in your class and to other classes.

17. Give the molecule a twist and the double helical nature of DNA is projected.

Analysis
18. Draw and label a section of the DNA model. List all of the characteristics of DNA in the model.

19. Measure the width of the DNA molecule in m and record in your lab notebook. The actual width of a DNA molecule is 2 nm, and in a human cell there are approximately 2 m of DNA. Calculate how long the DNA model would have to be to equal a ratio of 2 nm in width : 2m in length. (Remember to convert the metric system units properly!!)

20. Lambda virus DNA contains about 49,000 base pairs. What percentage of the total length of a Lambda virus is the DNA model? How long would the model have to be to represent Lambda?

Introduction

1. _____

2. _____

3. _____

4. _____;_____

5. _____

6. a)_____ c)_____

   b)_____ d) _____

Activity- Building a Scale Model of DNA

7. _____8. _____9. _____ 10. _____ 11. _____ 12. _____ a. _____ b. _____

13. _____ 14. _____ 15. _____ 16. _____ 17. _____

Analysis

18.

Characteristics=_____

19. Width of DNA model=_____m

20.

Restriction Analysis of Lambda DNA

Prelab

DNA is a long, thin molecule containing hundreds or thousands of genes along its length. Manipulating DNA was an extremely difficult process until the discovery of restriction endonucleases, enzymes which cut DNA predictably and precisely at the same place every time. The place where a restriction enzyme cuts is called a restriction site. The discrete bands of DNA seen on a gel represent more than a billion like-sized fragments, all of which have been cut in exactly the same place. In restriction analysis, the bands can be analyzed for size, sequence, mass, etc.

When a length of DNA is cut by a restriction enzyme, a number of discrete segments is produced.

Since DNA is negatively charged (phosphates), it will move through a gel to the positive pole. DNA bands move according to size. The smaller a piece of DNA, the faster it will travel through the gel.

Diagram 1

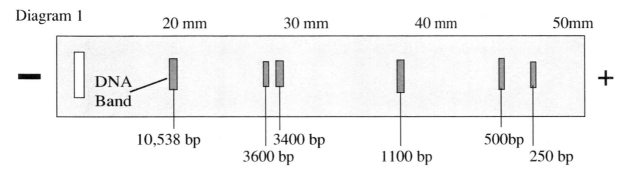

Determining Logarithms

All of the 1 billion+ pieces of DNA in a discrete band will have the same number of base pairs. Since the range of DNA segment lengths usually varies over several powers of 10, the base pair number is often converted to a logarithm. The logarithm of a number is that number expressed as a power of 10.

Examples:

$$\log \text{ of } 10{,}538 = 4.02 = 10^{4.02} \qquad \log \text{ of } 250 = 2.39 = 10^{2.39}$$

Antilogs can also be found:
antilog of 3.53 = 3400   antilog of 2.698 = 500

Questions

1. What is found along DNA?
2. What is a restriction endonuclease?
3. Where does a restriction enzyme cut?
4. What can be analyzed in restriction analysis?
5. Why does DNA move through a gel?
6. What determines how far a DNA band moves through a gel?
7. What is the total length in base pairs of the DNA segment in the example above?
8. Do the problems on your Laboratory Data Sheet.

Laboratory- Restriction Analysis of Phage Lambda DNA

Materials (per group)

Power supply, gel box, lambda restriction digests using BstE II, HindIII and Eco RI; uncut DNA, 1% agarose, TBE running buffer, 10 µl pipettes and tips, loading dye, ruler, semilog graph paper, scientific calculator, pencil, 1.5 mL microfuge tubes, microfuge, crushed ice, 400 mL beaker, permanent marker, gloves; For the class: gel illuminator, camera, film, DNA stain

Procedure   (Wear gloves throughout the procedure.)

9. Pour the 1% agarose gels and let them solidify.

10. Label and prepare four microfuge tubes according to the matrix below. **Keep the tubes on ice!!**

	Pre-Digested DNA	DI water	Loading Dye
Tube 1	1µl EcoRI	8µl	1µl
Tube 2	1µl BstE II	8µl	1µl
Tube 3	1µl Hind III	8µl	1µl
Tube 4	1µl uncut DNA	8µl	1µl

11. Cover the gel with TBE running buffer until it is just immersed.

12. Pulse centrifuge the tubes for 5 seconds, then load the entire contents of tubes 1, 2, 3, and 4 onto the gel-- each into a separate well. (Diagram 2)

13. Put on the lid, and turn the power supply to 110 volts. After letting the gel run for 90 minutes, turn off the power supply, open the gel box, and remove the gel.

14. Stain the gel according to teacher direction. Take a picture of the gel.

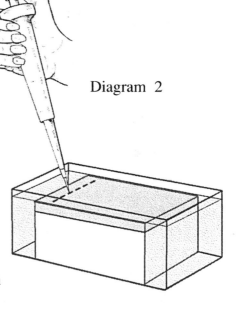

Diagram 2

Analysis

15. On the picture, measure the distance in mm from the well to each band for the 4 lanes and record in Table 1.
16. Your teacher will give you the bp lengths for BstE II. Convert them to logs and record in Table1.
17. Construct a graph on semilog graph paper of migration distance (mm) vs. log of the base pairs for BstE II. Find the best straight line through the dots.
18. Starting with the migration distance, use interpolation to find the logs of the restriction fragment base pairs for Hind *III and EcoRI. Record in Table 1.
19. Take the antilog and record the actual number of base pairs.
20. How many restriction sites did Eco RI have? BstE II? HindIII?
21. Why is the number of restriction sites different for each restriction enzyme?
22. According to the base pair numbers from EcoRI and BstE II, what is the total number of base pairs in Lambda DNA?

Restriction Analysis of Lambda DNA *Laboratory Data Sheet*

Prelab

1. _____

2. _____

3. _____

4. _____

5. _____

6. _____

7. _____

8a. log of 2700 = _____   b. log of 878= _____

  c. Antilog of 3.8= _____   d. Antilog of 2.1= _____

  e. Lambda DNA was cut with the same restriction enzyme, which yielded the
   following restriction fragments:

```
        A        |              B               | C  | D
_____|_____|____|____
                 |                               |    |
```

On the gel below draw where you could expect to see the bands corresponding to the restriction
fragments.

Laboratory- Restriction Analysis of Phage Lambda DNA

9. _____   10. _____   11. _____

12. _____   13. _____   14. _____

Analysis

Table 1.

Band	HindIII			BstE II			EcoRI			uncut DNA		
	mm	bp	log	mm	bp	log	mm	bp	log	mm	bp	log

15. _____

16. _____

17. _____

18. _____

19. _____

18. Interpolation: Start with a known migration distance. Draw a straight line up to the HindIII line. Draw a line to the Y axis. Record the log. Take the antilog to get the actual number of base pairs.

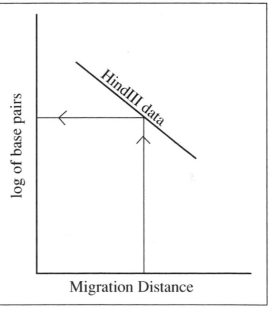

20. EcoR1 =_____   BstE II =_____   HindIII =_____

21. _____

_____

22. _____

The Effect of UV Light on DNA

Prelab

UV light is a type of nonionizing radiation which can damage DNA. When UV light strikes DNA, it can cut one or both strands, leaving two types of breaks in the DNA. This breakage is particularly apparent when using plasmid DNA, since it is in the form of a circle. If one strand of the plasmid DNA is struck by UV light, an open circle results. If both strands of the DNA are cut, a linear form of DNA results. The uncut DNA remains in the supercoiled form.

Diagram 1.

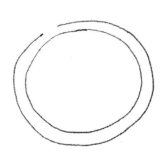

Supercoiled DNA   1 Strand Break- Open Circle Form   2 Strand Breaks-- Linear Form

Diagram 2.

On a gel, the three species of DNA appear as shown below.

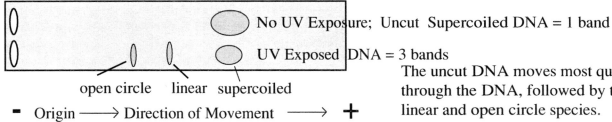

No UV Exposure; Uncut Supercoiled DNA = 1 band

UV Exposed DNA = 3 bands

open circle   linear   supercoiled

The uncut DNA moves most quicky through the DNA, followed by the linear and open circle species.

■ Origin ⟶ Direction of Movement ⟶ ✚

Questions
1. What kind of radiation is UV light?
2. Why is plasmid DNA used to study the effects of UV light on DNA?
3. If DNA remains uncut, what form results?
4. If one strand of DNA is cut, which form results?
5. If two strands of DNA are cut, which form results?
6. Draw a gel and place the 3 forms in order on the gel.

Laboratory- The Effect of UV Light on Plasmid DNA

Materials
NIH Image Software, TBE (Tris-borate-EDTA) running buffer, gel box, agarose, power supply, pipette, DNA stain, loading dye, UV light, Two 1.5 mL microfuge tubes containing plasmid DNA/ Water mixture, 10 1.5mL microfuge tubes, fine-tipped permanent marker, latex gloves, 2 trays containing ice, microfuge, gel illuminator, camera, film, **goggles which block UV light.**

Caution: Always wear goggles when working with UV light. Make sure your eye wear is UV opaque! UV light can damage the retina!

Procedure *Wear gloves + goggles at all times!! Remember to keep the DNA on ice at all times!!*
7. Cast 1% agarose gels.

8. Get two tubes containing the DNA/water mixture. Label one tube 'UV' and the other 'Control.'
   Remember to keep the DNA on ice at all times!!
9. Label five 1.5 ml microfuge tubes UV 0, UV 10 min, UV 20 min, UV 30 min, UV 40 min. Label five more 1.5 microfuge tubes Control 0, Control 10, Control 20, Control 30, Control 40.

10. Remove 9μl from the UV tube, place the sample in the 1.5 mL tube labeled UV 0 and place on ice. Repeat this procedure for the Control Tube.

11. Open the 1.5 ml tube labeled UV and place it 10 cm under the UV light in ice. (Diag. 3) Turn on the lamp. Open the Control tube and place on ice away from the UV.

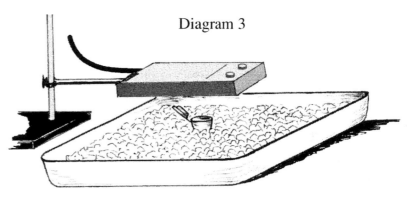

Diagram 3

12. After 10 minutes, remove a 9 μl sample from the UV tube and place it in the microfuge tube labeled UV 10 min. Repeat this procedure for the Control sample.

An aluminum foil shield can be placed over the light.

13. Continue taking 9μl samples at 10 minutes intervals from both the UV experimental and the Control sample. Stop at 40 minutes.

14. Add 1 μl of loading dye to each microfuge tube.

15. Pulse spin in a microfuge for 5 seconds.

16. Pour 1X TBE buffer until the level just immerses the gels, load the DNA samples into the gel, and turn the power supply to approximately 15-20 volts. Let the gel run for 12-13 hours.

Day 2   Day 2   Day 2
17. Stain the gels according to teacher directions, and take a picture of the gel.

Analysis
18. Using NIH Image software, find the amount of linear, open circle, and supercoiled (uncut) DNA in each band. Write the amounts of the linear, open circle, and super coiled DNA forms in Table 1.

19. Graph the DNA amounts vs time.

20. What happens to the amount of supercoiled, linear, and open circle DNA as the time of UV irradiation increases? Why?

166

The Effect of UV Light on DNA   *Laboratory Data Sheet*

Prelab

1. _____

2. _____

3. _____

4. _____

5. _____

6. _____

Laboratory- The Effect of UV Light on Plasmid DNA

7. _____ 8. _____ 9. _____ 10. _____ 11. _____ 12. _____ 13. _____ 14. _____

15. _____   16. _____

Day 2

17. _____

Analysis

18. _____

Table 1.   Pixel Area   (from NIH Image)

Time(min)	0		10		20		30		40	
	Con.	UV	Con.	UV	Con.	UV	Con.	UV	Con.	UV
Supercoiled										
Linear										
Open Circle										

19.

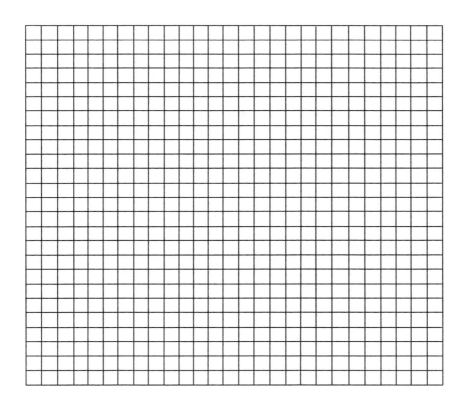

20. _____

_____

Correlations

Prelab

Scientists often want to determine whether two sets data are co-related, that is, if there is a linear relationship between two variables X and Y such that a change in X causes a predictable change in Y. Such a linear mathematical relationship is called a correlation. Determining whether a correlation exists between two variables can be a powerful tool to predict the future outcome of a particular event.

Given two sets of related data, there are three possible outcomes for correlations:

> A positive correlation means that a large X corresponds to a large Y.
> A negative correlation means that a large X corresponds to a small Y.
> No correlation exists if a change in Y is not predictable from a change in X.

Calculating whether a correlation exists usually starts by plotting a scatter diagram to determine whether a linear relationship exists between X and Y.

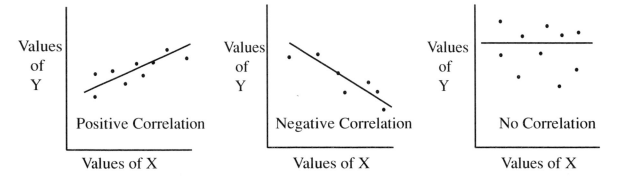

| Positive Correlation | Negative Correlation | No Correlation |

A strong positive correlation will have a value of 1 or nearly 1, while a negative correlation will have a value of -1 or nearly -1. If no linear relationship exists between X and Y the correlation value will be 0 or near to 0. The correlation value is designated as the letter r and $-1 \leq r \leq 1$.

Example

A scientist wants to determine if a correlation exists between temperature and the number of cricket chirps. She goes into the field and collects the following data:

Temperature °C	#Chirps
12	22
17	36
13	25
18	33
16	33
20	42
19	40
14	28
15	26
21	40

First determine if a linear relationship exists using a scatter plot.

The graph shows that x and y appear to be linearly related.

Since x and y appear to be linearly related, the formula to calculate the correlation can be used. The formula to calculate the correlation (r) is:

$$r = \frac{n\,(\Sigma\, xy)\; -\;(\Sigma\, x)\,(\Sigma\, y)}{\sqrt{n\,(\Sigma\, x^2)\; -\;(\Sigma\, x)^2}\;\;\sqrt{n\,(\Sigma\, y^2)\; -\;(\Sigma\, y)^2}}$$

where: Σ=sum of
n= number of
paired observations

Although the formula looks somewhat imposing, it is actually easy to use:

Temperature °C (x)	#Chirps(y)	x^2	y^2	xy
12	22	144	484	264
17	36	289	1296	612
13	25	169	625	325
18	33	324	1089	594
16	33	256	1089	528
20	42	400	1764	840
19	40	361	1600	760
14	28	196	784	392
15	26	225	676	390
21	40	441	1600	840
Σx =165	Σy = 325	Σx^2 =2805	Σy^2=11,007	Σxy=5545

$$r = \frac{10\,(5545)\; -\;(165)\,(325)}{\sqrt{10\,(2805)\; -\;(165)^2}\;\;\sqrt{10\,(11{,}007) - (325)^2}}$$

$r = \dfrac{1825}{1913}$ r= .95   The formula tells you if the correlation is positive or negative. Since .95 is close to 1 = strong correlation.

The formula $r^2 100$ = the percentage of the total variation of the y's which is accounted for by the relationship with x. In the example above $(.95)^2\,100 = 91\%$. Therefore 91% of the variation in y is accounted for by a linear relationship to x. An r above .75 (or <-.75) is typically a strong correlation.

Problems
1. Draw and label positive, negative, and 0 correlation scatter diagrams on your Lab Data Sheet.
2. How is a correlation mathematically described?
3. Do the practice problem on your Lab Data Sheet.

Laboratory- What is the Correlation of Foot Size to Height in Males and Females?
Materials
Meter stick, calculator, paper
Procedure
4. Measure each other's height and foot size (without shoes) in cm. and write them on the board under either male or female. On a separate piece of paper copy the final results.
5. Graph height and foot size for males and females in Graph 1. Is there a linear relationship?
6. Do the correlation calculations for males and females. Use a separate sheet of paper if necessary.
Analysis
7. Use the $r^2 100$ formula to determine whether there is a stronger correlation among males or females for height and foot size. How do you know?

Correlations

Prelab

1.

2. _____

   _____

3. A researcher wants to determine if a correlation exists between femur length and the distance a frog can jump. He gathers the following data:

Femur Length (cm)	Distance of Jump (cm)
4.3	32
2.0	28
2.4	29
3.0	25
3.5	38
2.5	23
3.2	26
3.8	41
4.5	38
4.1	37

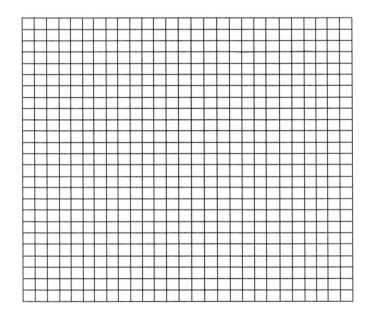

Calculate the correlation between femur length and jump distance:

3. (Con'd) Correlation=_____ Total variation = $r^2 100$ = _____

Discuss the strength of correlation: _____

_____

Laboratory- What is the Correlation of Foot Size to Height in Males and Females?

4._____

5.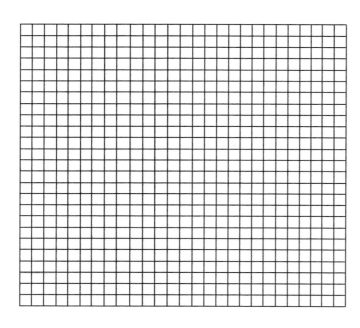

6. Correlation Calculations:

Analysis

7. Total variation for males = $r^2 100$ =_____ ; total variation for females = $r^2 100$=_____

_____

The Central Tendencies of Data

Prelab

For any trait or characteristic in a species, there can be wide differences in length, width, mass, and coloration which contribute to variation in that species. Biologists might wish to know how much the average lengths of two snake populations of the same species differ —how much variation there is among that species. Simple statistics can help quantify variation. The Central Tendency of a set of numbers describes the location of a set of values. Four measurements of the Central Tendency will be applied in this laboratory: Range, Mean, Median, and Mode.

1. **Range** = Difference between the highest and lowest value. Range = Highest value - lowest value	3. **Median** = The middle value in a set of numbers in rank order: Median = $\dfrac{n+1}{2}$ n= sample size number in the rank order
2. **Mean** = (Average) The mean is the sum of a set of values divided by the number of samples. Mean = $Y = \dfrac{\sum Y}{n}$ n= total no. of samples $\sum Y$= sum of Y values Y = Sample mean	4. **Mode** = The value which occurs most often in a set of data.

Outliers are values which are far below or above the range.

Example: 30 students take a test worth 50 points. Their scores in rank order were:

20,21,21,23,23,26,26,27,27,28,29,31,31,32,32,33,33,34,34,34,34,35,35,36,36,37,38,38,42,43

Find the range, mean, median, and mode for the test scores.

A. The Range = Highest value - lowest value   The range of values = 20-->43
   Range = 43-20 = 23

B. The Mean = $Y = \dfrac{\sum Y}{n}$ 20+21+21+23+23+26+26+27+27+28+29+31+31+32+32+33+33+34+34+34+34+
   35+35+36+36+37+38+38+42+43 = 939   939/30 = 31.3

C. Median = $\dfrac{n+1}{2}$ = $\dfrac{30+1}{2}$ = 15.5 Count 15.5 units from the beginning:
                                 Median = 32.5

   20,21,21,23,23,26,26,27,27,28,29,31,31,32,32, ↓ 33,33,34,34,34,34,35,35,36,36,37,38,38,42,43

D. Mode = The value which occurs most often. The number 34 occurs 4 times = mode.

   20,21,21,23,23,26,26,27,27,28,29,31,31,32,32,33,33|34,34,34,34|35,35,36,36,37,38,38,42,43

Graphing
Statistical data can also be represented on a graph.

Test Score Range	# of Students
16-20	1
21-25	4
26-30	6
31-35	12
36-40	5
41-45	2

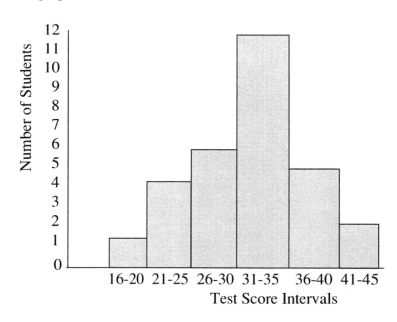

The Bell Curve
If you were to draw a line connecting the bars, it would reveal a distinct shape. This shape represents a unique distribution of numbers called the Bell Curve.

Questions
1. Do the problem on your Lab Data Sheet.

Laboratory- A Quantitative Analysis of Human Height
Materials
Meter stick (or metric measuring tape), pencil or pen, graph paper.

Procedure
2. Measure your height in cm., then record it on the board. Copy the student heights into Table 1 on the Lab Data Sheet.

3. Calculate the range, mean, median, and mode for student heights in the class and record on the Lab Data Sheet.

4. Fill in Table 2 on your Lab Data Sheet with the appropriate data. Extend the table if necessary.

5. Using 'Height Range' on the X axis and '# of students' on the Y axis, graph the heights of the students in your class. Use 5 cm height ranges.

Analysis
6. What do the range, mean, median, and mode tell you about the students' heights in your class?

The Central Tendencies of Data   *Laboratory Data Sheet*

Prelab

Questions

1. Given the following data set, determine the a) Range, b) Mean, c) Median, and d) Mode.

The necks of 32 giraffes were measured in m and the following data were recorded:

1.55, 1.73, 1.66, 1.56, 1.55, 1.87, 1.83, 1.86, 1.79, 1.84, 1.93, 1.83, 1.97, 1.83, 1.92, 2.05,
1.87, 1.83, 1.83, 2.03, 1.97, 1.94, 1.88, 1.88, 1.72, 1.66, 1.68, 1.77, 1.73, 1.78, 1.73, 1.65

Range

Mean

Median

Mode

Graphing

Fill in the following table, then graph the data:

Giraffe Neck Length Range (m)	# of Giraffes in this Range
1.5-1.59	
1.6-1.69	
1.7-1.79	
1.8-1.89	
1.9-1.99	
2.0-2.09	

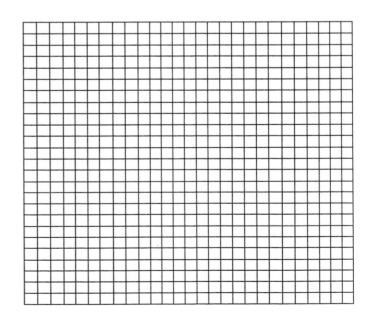

Laboratory- A Quantitative Analysis of Human Height

2. _____

Student Height- Fill in the following table with the heights of students in your class in m.
Table 1.

Rank Order of Student Heights =_____

_____

_____

3.   Range=

_____

     Mean

_____

     Median

_____

     Mode

_____

4.

Height Range (5cm)	# of Students in Range

Table 2.

5.

Analysis

6. _____

Analyzing a Normal Distribution

Prelab

In any large population of the same species, there can be variability in length, mass, height and other characteristics. Biologists can use statistics on a sample of that population to make estimates about the entire population. Members of a sample are randomly selected individuals from the population.

Calculating Variability

Variance- is a measure of the degree of dispersion among the data. Dispersion is the arrangement of a series of data points around the mean of a distribution. Variability refers to the extent of that dispersion.

It is calculated:

$$S^2 = \frac{\sum (Y - \overline{Y})^2}{n - 1}$$

Where:
$\sum$ = sum of
Y = Y value
$\overline{Y}$ = sample mean
n = total number of samples

Standard Deviation- This is the distance away from the mean the members of a sample are.

$$S = \sqrt{\frac{\sum (Y - \overline{Y})^2}{n - 1}}$$

Where:
Y = Y value
$\overline{Y}$ = sample mean
n = total number of samples
S = standard deviation

Z Score- The z score indicates how many standard deviations the sample is from the mean.

$$z = \frac{Y - \overline{Y}}{S}$$

Where:
Y = value of the sample
$\overline{Y}$ = mean for the population
S = standard deviation

Normal Distribution- represents a sample distribution under a symmetrical, bell-shaped curve. The whole area under the curve is equal to 1, and a discrete, or defined, area under the curve is the likelihood that each probability will occur.

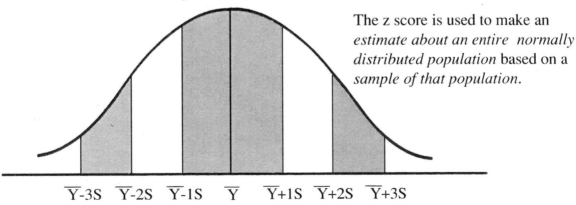

The z score is used to make an *estimate about an entire normally distributed population* based on a *sample of that population.*

$$\overline{Y}-3S \quad \overline{Y}-2S \quad \overline{Y}-1S \quad \overline{Y} \quad \overline{Y}+1S \quad \overline{Y}+2S \quad \overline{Y}+3S$$

Example: Find the mean and standard deviation for the following set of height data:
Heights (cm) 159, 157, 155, 162, 172, 145, 167, 165, 180, 158

$$\text{Mean} = \frac{159 + 157 + 155 + 162 + 172 + 145 + 167 + 165 + 180 + 158}{10} = 162 \text{ cm}$$

Standard Deviation = $S = \sqrt{\dfrac{\sum (Y - \overline{Y})^2}{n - 1}}$

$\sqrt{\dfrac{846}{10 - 1}} = 9.7$

The Standard Deviation = 9.7

Y - $\overline{Y}$	(Y - $\overline{Y}$)²
159 - 162 = -3	9
157 - 162 = -5	25
155 - 162 = -7	49
162 - 162 = 0	0
172 - 162 = 10	100
145 - 162 = -17	289
167 - 162 = 5	25
165 - 162 = 3	9
180 - 162 = 18	324
158 - 162 = -4	16
Total =	846

The Z Score- Example 1

The z score is used to make *estimates about an entire population* based on a *sample of that population*. Suppose you wanted to know what percentage of the *entire population* is betweem 162 and 170 cm tall *based on the sample in the example*. The z score provides this information.

$z = \dfrac{Y - \overline{Y}}{S} = \dfrac{|170 - 162|}{9.7} = \dfrac{8}{9.7} = .82$ ∴ 170 is .82 of a standard deviation away from 162

When .82 is checked on the z score chart (See Appendix 1b) it corresponds to an area under the curve of .29, meaning *29% of the population* lies between a range of 162 cm and 170 cm.

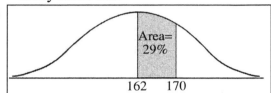

TheZ Score-Example 2

What proportion of this *population* is 175 cm or taller?

$z = \dfrac{175 - 162}{9.7} = 1.34 = .41$ on the z score chart

$\begin{array}{r} .5000 \\ -.4100 \\ \hline .0900 \end{array}$ (area of 1/2 the curve)

∴ 9% of the population is taller than 175 cm.

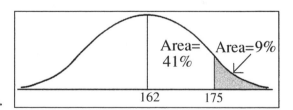

Questions

1. Do the practice problem on your Lab Data Sheet.

Laboratory- A Statistical Analysis of Height

Materials

Meter sticks, calculator, pen or pencil

Procedure

2. Follow the directions on the Lab Data Sheet.

3. Find the mean, standard deviation, and z score for height data from your class.

Analysis

4. Answer questions on the Lab Data Sheet.

178

Analyzing a Normal Distribution   *Laboratory Data Sheet*

Prelab

1. A stand of 30 trees growing in the same area under the same conditions was measured and the following data were recorded: Height in m: 5.6, 4.7, 5.6, 7.1, 6.7, 5.8, 4.9, 5.7, 6.3, 6.7, 6.3, 6.0, 6.1, 5.7, 4.8, 6.5, 7.0, 5.7, 6.2, 6.4, 5.5, 5.9, 5.7, 5.8, 5.1, 5.2, 5.3, 5.3, 5.5, 5.4

   a. Make a histogram of these data using .5 m intervals (ex. = 4.6m-5.0m) on the X axis and number of trees on the Y axis.

Table 1.

.5 m Interval	# of Trees

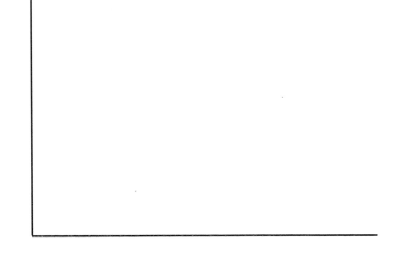

   b. On a *separate piece of paper* make a table to include columns for Y-$\overline{Y}$ and (Y - $\overline{Y}$)^2 data. Assume a normal distribution for the population of trees. Find the mean, standard deviation, and z score for the sample. Use the <u>sample</u> data to estimate what percentage of the <u>population</u> is: 1) taller than 7.0 m. 2) shorter than 6.5m. See Appendix 1b for z scores.

Laboratory- A Statistical Analysis of Height

2. *On a separate piece of paper make a table (**Table 2**)* to record the height of each student in the class. Measure your height in cm, and record it in Table 2 and on the board. Record the heights of the other students in Table 2.

2a. Fill in Table 3 below with the appropriate height data. Make a histogram of intervals vs. # of students.

Table 3.

Height Interval 5 cm	# of Students in Interval

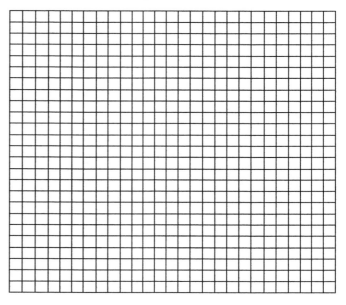

3. On a separate piece of paper make a table (Table 4) with columns for $Y - \overline{Y}$ and $(Y - \overline{Y})^2$. Copy your height and those of the other students from Table 2 into this table under Y.

3a. Find the mean for your class and record it. _____

    Calculate the standard deviation and record it. _____

Analysis

4. From your class sample, use z scores to estimate what percentage of the entire population is:
    a) taller than 165 cm.   b) shorter than 170 cm.

BEAIMs

Dealing with Data

Making Tables

Construct tables which organize the following information.

1. Each year for 5 years the growth of a tree was measured. Year 1 - .7m; year 2 - 2.0 m; year 3 - 2.6m; year 4 - 3.1m; year 5 - 4.2m

2. Kilograms of apples picked were recorded over 10 years. 1972-1981 = 21,34,23,12,45,23,43,23,76,34

3. The number of cricket chirps was recorded at various temperatures. (Temp. in Celsius)
   Night 1- Temp.= 16, cricket chirps = 33; T= 18, chirps = 38; T = 20, chirps = 42; Temp= 22, Chirps =46; Temp.= 24, Chirps= 50.   Night 2 Temp.= 16, Chirps= 32; Temp. = 18, Chirps =36; Temp.= 20, Chirps= 41; Temp.= 22, Chirps= 43; Temp.= 24, Chirps= 51

4. Over a period of 5 days, a researcher kept track of the number of male and female normal and vestigial winged flies that were born in her laboratory.
   Day 1- 2 normal males, 3 normal females, 0 vestigial males, 0 vestigial females
   Day 2- 3 normal males, 3 normal females, 1 vestigial males, 0 vestigial females
   Day 3- 2 normal males, 1 normal female, 1 vestigial male, 1 vestigial female
   Day 4- 1 normal male, 1 normal female, 1 vestigial male, 1 vestigial female
   Day 5- 0 normal male, 1 normal female, 2 vestigial males, 1 vestigial female

5. Chargaff, a researcher who studied DNA, got the following data when he looked at the relative amounts of the bases guanine (G), cytosine (C), adenine (A), and thymine in human and pig spleen and liver cells.

   Human spleen - A= 29.2; G= 21; T= 29.4; C= 20.4
   Human liver cells- A= 30.3; G= 19.5; T= 30.3; C= 19.9

   Pig spleen cells- A = 29.6; G= 20.4; T= 29.2; C= 20.8
   Pig liver cells-   A= 29.4; G= 20.5; T= 29.7; C= 20.5

6. A researcher was looking at the rate of increase of a population of beetles in a corn field. The data:

   Trial 1: generation 1= 2 beetles; gen. 2= 5 beetles; gen. 3= 9 beetles; gen. 4= 17 beetles; gen. 5 = 36 beetles; gen. 6= 75 beetles; gen. 7 = 131 beetles; gen. 8= 262 beetles.

   Trial 2: gen. 1 = 3 beetles; gen. 2= 6 beetles; gen. 3= 10 beetles; gen. 4 = 20 beetles; gen. 5= 40 beetles; gen. 6 = 71 beetles; gen. 7 = 140 beetles; gen. 8= 280 beetles

7. A zoologist was looking at 2 species of lizards that were inhabiting a rock in the desert. Each hour the temperature and number of each lizard were recorded.

Hour 1- temp. = 17C, species A= 3, species B= 7; Hour 2- temp.- 22C, species A = 4, species B= 10; Hour 3- temp. = 26, species A = 4, species B= 12; Hour 4- temp. = 31, species A= 11, species B= 4; Hour 5- temp.= 34, species A = 13, species B = 4; Hour 6- temp. = 35, species = A, species B = 3

8. A burial ground containing a number of skeletons was discovered by archeologists. The age of the skeletons was estimated.
Newborn infants= 12; less than 2 years old = 15; 2-6 years of age= 2; 6-18 years old= 15; 18-21 years of age= 1; 21-50 years of age = 36; 50+ years of age= 7

9. A researcher was looking at the percentage of different blood types in different races- African, Caucasian, and Asian
African- Type A- 42%, B= 25, AB = 3, 0 = 30;   Whites - Type A = 37%, B= 27%, AB = 2, 0= 34; Asian - Type A= 25, B= 23, AB= 10; 0= 42

10. A scientist was comparing the percentage of ammonia, urea, and uric acid in various organisms.

   planaria- ammonia= 100%, urea= 0, uric acid = 0
   squid- ammonia= 67%, urea = 2%, uric = 2%
   frog tadpole- ammonia= 74%, urea=20%, uric acid= 0
   human- ammonia = 4, urea = 84%, uric acid =2%
   insects- ammonia = 0, urea = 0, uric acid = 92%

Graphing

Graphs are diagrams representing numerical data. There are many types of graphs, but two types will be the focus of this section--bar and line graphs--since they are used frequently in biology.

A graph is composed of two lines, the horizontal (X) axis and the vertical (Y) axis. The X axis is often referred to as the independent variable and the Y axis as the dependent variable.

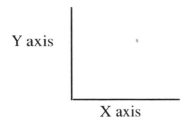

Y axis

X axis

There are four essential components in constructing a graph:
1) Select whether a bar or line graph should be used.
2) Select which numbers or items get placed on the horizontal and vertical axes.
3) Select the parameters of the graph.
4) Make sure the graph axes are labeled and the graph is titled.

Two examples will be used to illustrate graphing techniques.

Example 1: Bar Graph
In an orchard the following number of kilograms of apples were picked during five years.

Year	Kilograms
1990	54
1991	45
1992	62
1993	39
1994	34

1. Graphs are typically made from data organized in a table. Should a bar graph or line graph be used in this case? Since the number of kilograms of apples picked each year is independent of the year before or after, a bar graph would typically be used.

2. Determine which information gets placed on the horizontal and vertical axes. What is known in advance, fixed in advanced or does not change (independent variable) goes on the horizontal (X) axis. Since the years are known in advance, they go on the X axis. The number of kilograms of apples varies (dependent variable) so they go on the Y axis.

3. Years = 90-94; The number of kilograms of apples varies from a low of 34 to a high of 62. **Since the numbers of kilos of apples is not evenly spaced the numbers in the tables cannot be used. Evenly spaced numbers must be used! In this case increments of 5 will be used, starting with 30 and ending with 65, since these numbers include all numbers in the data.**

4. The X axis is labeled with the year and the Y axis with Kg of Apples and a title is added.

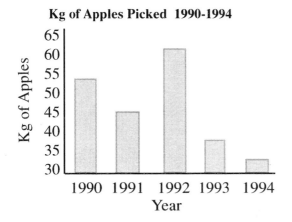

Kg of Apples Picked 1990-1994

Example 2: Line Graph

The following data were recorded for the growth of a plant:

Day	Cm
0	0
1	2.0
2	6.3
3	8.4
4	11
5	15.5
6	18.2
7	19.1
8	19.4

1. Line graphs are typically used when the independent variable affects the dependent variable. In this case, the growth of the plant is dependent on the growth of the previous day.

2. Since the days are known in advance they are placed on the horizontal axis. Growth is the dependent variable since it is not known in advance.

3. The number of days ranges from 0 -8. The cm of growth ranges from 0-19.4 Graph parameters will be chosen which include numbers 0-19.4 using evenly spaced increments. Any evenly spaced increments can be used, **but not the numbers in the table. The increments could be 2, 3, 4, 5, etc. For this example, 2 will be used, going from 0-20**

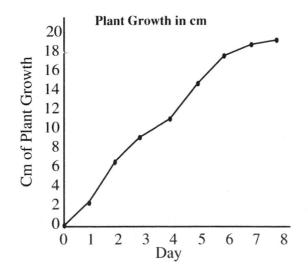

4. The X axis is labeled with the day and the Y axis is labeled with cm of Plant Growth. The title is added.

Problems

1. After making the appropriate tables, graph the data for numbers 1, 2, 6, 8, and 9 in the Making Tables section using either a bar or line graph.

184

Stem and Leaf Plots

These plots are extremely useful for comparing two sets of data. They can be prepared with little background in graphing.

Example: Using a Stem and Leaf Plot

Sample Data: Scores for Safety Test
43, 27, 23, 35, 15, 23 ,17, 24, 28, 9, 31, 19, 35, 17, 37, 22, 24, 25, 34

1. Find the smallest and the largest data values. The digits in the largest comparable places in these value will form the base and apex of the stem.

    ex.   9 is the smallest and 43 is the largest

            the tens place is the largest comparable digit

            9 has an 0 in the ten's place and 43 has a 4 in the ten's place

            the st*em w*ill be the digits from 0 to 4

2. Write the stem vertically with a line to their right.

```
0|
1|
2|
3|
4|
```

3. Separate each value into a stem and a leaf with the leaves being the digits to the right of the largest comparable digit. Place the leaves on the plot to the right of the stem.

```
0|9
1|
2|
3|
4|3
```

4. Continue to separate each value this way. The order of the numbers does not matter.

```
0|9
1|5797
2|73348245
3|51574
4|3
```

5. Rotating the plot 90 degrees produces a bar graph.

6. A second set of data can be plotted on the left of the stem to produce a comparable graph.

7. The shape of the plot can be instructive for class discussion (bell, U, J, rectangle).

Box and Whiskers Plots

Box and Whisker plots are useful for quickly determining the median, quartiles and extremes of a large set of data and for comparing more than two sets of data. They require very little in terms of math and graphing skills.

Example: Using a Box and Whiskers Plot

Sample Data: Scores for Safety Test   (Same data as used in Stem and Leaf example)
        43, 27, 23, 35, 15, 23 ,17, 24, 28, 9, 31, 19, 35, 17, 37, 22, 24, 25, 34

1. Find the median (middle value). Mark this on an appropriate number line.

```
        |
  _____
  5   10  15  20  25  30  35  40  45
```

2. Find the medians of the upper half and the lower half. These will form the delineations between the 1st and 2nd quartiles and the 3rd and 4th quartiles. Mark these on the number line.

```
         |  |        |
  _____
  5   10  15  20  25  30  35  40  45
```

3. Find the lower and upper extremes and mark them on the number line.

```
    •    |  |        |    •
  _____
  5   10  15  20  25  30  35  40  45
```

4. Draw a box between the two quartiles. Mark the median with a line across the box. Draw two whiskers from the quartiles to the extremes.

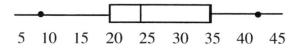

```
    •    |___|_____|    •
  5   10  15  20  25  30  35  40  45
```

5. Questions to ask:
    a. What percent of the values are:
            below the median? below the lower quartile? etc.
    b. Why is one whisker longer than the other?
    c. Why isn't the median in the center of the box?
    d. What are the reasons for the distribution of the data?

6. List the variables which potentially affect the results and choose one to control. Repeat the experiment and redo the Box and Whiskers plot. Compare with the first B&W and reanalyze the data.

7. This allows students to get immediate feedback as to the quality of their data, to develop an understanding of the concept of experimental control, and to use this understanding to improve their laboratory work and thus their results.

Significant Figures

In every measurement there is likely to be an error or uncertainty factor due to the imprecise measuring ability of the instrument used. Suppose you want to find the mass of a coin. Using a regular balance that finds mass to the tenth of a gram you find the coin is 26.5g plus or minus 0.1g. The uncertain value is the last digit so the coin could be 26.6g or 26.4g. We can reduce our uncertainty by using a more precise balance, but there will still be that last digit that is uncertain.

When the results of measurement are recorded, the uncertainty should also be indicated to show the preciseness of the work.

Uncertainty may be indicated with the plus or minus (+ / -) but more commonly it is understood that there is uncertainty in the last digit and the value is simply stated by itself. So a measurement of 26.517g indicates an uncertainty of 0.001g.

Rules of Significant Figures

All the certain digits of a measurement plus the estimated digit are considered significant figures.

Rule 1   All non-zero digits are significant, and any zeros between non-zero digits.
17.34g has 4 significant figures.   10.01 has 4 significant figures.

Rule 2   If the number is one or greater and has a decimal point, then all zeros are significant.   5.00g has 3 significant figures, but 500 is one.

Rule 3   If the number is one or greater and has no decimal point then all zeros to the right of the last digit are not significant, just place holders. (unless indicated) 10,400 g has 3 significant figures, but 104.00 has 5 significant figures and $1040\bar{0}$ has 5 significant figures.

A bar above a zero makes it significant meaning it was measured to that precision.

Rule 4   If the number is less than one then all zeros to the left of digits are not significant, just place holders. 0.0014 has 2 significant figures and 0.00140 has 3 significant figures.

Rule 5   Any number that represents a numerical count, (an exact definition), has an infinite number of significant figures.   e.g. 3 people

Calculations

In Addition and Subtraction the answer should reflect the numbers with the least precise measurement.
32.511 + 10.1 = 42.6   least precise is to the tenth
In Multiplication and Division the answer should reflect the numbers with the fewest significant figures.
7.13 X .32 = 2.3   fewest is 2 significant so the answer is rounded.

BEAIMs

Appendices

Appendix 1a: Distribution of χ^2

Probability

N	.99	.90	.80	.70	.50	.30	.20	.10	.05	.02	.01	.001
1	.0000157	.0158	.0642	.148	.455	1.074	1.642	2.706	3.841	5.412	6.635	10.827
2	.0201	.211	.446	.713	1.386	2.408	3.219	4.605	5.991	7.824	9.210	13.815
3	.115	.584	1.005	1.424	2.366	3.665	4.642	6.251	7.815	9.837	11.345	16.268
4	.297	1.064	1.649	2.195	3.357	4.878	5.989	7.779	9.488	11.668	13.277	18.465
5	.554	1.610	2.343	3.000	4.351	6.064	7.289	9.236	11.070	13.388	15.086	20.517
6	.872	2.204	3.070	3.828	5.348	7.231	8.558	10.645	12.592	15.033	16.812	22.457
7	1.239	2.833	3.822	4.671	6.346	8.383	9.803	12.017	14.067	16.622	18.475	24.322
8	1.646	3.490	4.594	5.527	7.344	9.524	11.030	13.362	15.507	18.168	20.090	26.125
9	2.088	4.168	5.380	6.393	8.343	10.656	12.242	14.684	16.919	19.679	21.666	27.877
10	2.558	4.865	6.179	7.267	9.342	11.781	13.442	15.987	18.307	21.161	23.209	29.588
11	3.053	5.578	6.989	8.148	10.341	12.899	14.631	17.275	19.675	22.618	24.725	31.624
12	3.571	6.304	7.807	9.034	11.340	14.011	15.812	18.549	21.026	24.054	26.217	32.909
13	4.107	7.042	8.634	9.926	12.340	15.119	16.985	19.812	22.362	25.472	27.688	34.528
14	4.660	7.790	9.467	10.821	13.339	16.222	18.151	21.064	23.685	26.873	29.141	36.123
15	5.229	8.547	10.307	11.721	14.339	17.322	19.311	22.307	24.996	28.259	30.578	37.697
16	5.812	9.312	11.152	12.624	15.338	18.418	20.465	23.542	26.296	29.633	32.000	39.252
17	6.408	10.085	12.002	13.531	16.338	19.511	21.615	24.769	27.587	30.995	33.409	40.790
18	7.015	10.865	12.857	14.440	17.338	20.601	22.760	25.989	28.869	32.346	34.805	42.312
19	7.633	11.651	13.716	15.352	18.338	21.689	23.900	27.204	30.144	33.687	36.191	43.820
20	8.260	12.443	14.578	16.266	19.337	22.775	25.038	28.412	31.410	35.020	37.566	45.315
21	8.897	13.240	15.445	17.182	30.337	23.858	26.171	29.615	32.671	36.343	38.932	46.797
22	9.542	14.041	16.314	18.101	21.337	24.939	27.301	30.813	33.924	37.659	40.289	48.268
23	10.196	14.848	17.187	19.021	22.337	26.018	28.429	32.007	35.172	38.968	41.638	49.728
24	10.856	15659	18.062	19.943	23.337	27.096	29.553	33.196	36.415	40.270	42.980	51.179
25	11.524	16.473	18.940	20.867	24.337	28.172	30.675	34.382	37.652	41.566	44.314	62.620
26	12.198	17.292	19.820	21.792	25.336	29.246	31.795	35.563	38.885	42.856	45.642	54.052
27	12.879	18.114	20.703	22.719	26.336	30.319	32.912	36.741	40.113	44.140	46.963	55.476
28	13.565	18.939	21.588	23.647	27.336	31.391	34.027	37.916	41.337	45.419	48.278	56.893
29	14.256	19.768	22.475	24.577	28.336	32.461	35.139	39.087	42.557	46.693	49.488	58.302
30	14.953	20.509	23.364	25.508	29.336	33.530	36.250	40.256	43.773	47.962	50.892	59.703

Appendix 1b-Area under the Normal Curve

Z	Area	Z	Area	Z	Area	Z	Area	Z	Area	Z	Area
.00	.0000	.51	.1950	1.02	.3461	1.53	.4370	2.04	.4788	2.55	.4946
.01	.0040	.52	.1985	1.03	.3485	1.54	.4382	2.05	.4798	2.56	.4948
.02	.0080	.53	.2019	1.04	.3508	1.55	.4394	2.06	.4803	2.57	.4949
.03	.0120	.54	.2054	1.05	.3531	1.56	.4406	2.07	.4808	2.58	.4951
.04	.0160	.55	.2088	1.06	.3554	1.57	.4418	2.08	.4812	2.59	.4952
.05	.0199	.56	.2123	1.07	.3577	1.58	.4429	2.09	.4817	2.60	.4953
.06	.0239	.57	.2157	1.08	.3599	1.59	.4441	2.10	.4821	2.61	.4955
.07	.0279	.58	.2190	1.09	.3621	1.60	.4452	2.11	.4826	2.62	.4956
.08	.0319	.59	.2224	1.10	.3643	1.61	.4463	2.12	.4830	2.63	.4957
.09	.0359	.60	.2257	1.11	.3665	1.62	.4474	2.13	.4834	2.64	.4959
.10	.0398	.61	.2291	1.12	.3686	1.63	.4484	2.14	.4838	2.65	.4960
.11	.0438	.62	.2324	1.13	.3709	1.64	.4495	2.15	.4842	2.66	.4961
.12	.0478	.63	.2357	1.14	.3729	1.65	.4505	2.16	.4846	2.67	.4962
.13	.0517	.64	.2389	1.15	.3749	1.66	.4515	2.17	.4850	2.68	.4963
.14	.0557	.65	.2422	1.16	.3770	1.67	.4525	2.18	.4854	2.69	.4964
.15	.0596	.66	.2454	1.17	.3790	1.68	.4535	2.19	.4857	2.70	.4965
.16	.0636	.67	.2486	1.18	.3810	1.69	.4545	2.20	.4861	2.71	.4966
.17	.0675	.68	.2517	1.19	.3830	1.70	.4554	2.21	.4864	2.72	.4967
.18	.0714	.69	.2549	1.20	.3849	1.71	.4564	2.22	.4868	2.73	.4968
.19	.0753	.70	.2580	1.21	.3869	1.72	.4573	2.23	.4871	2.74	.4969
.20	.0793	.71	.2611	1.22	.3888	1.73	.4582	2.24	.4875	2.75	.4970
.21	.0832	.72	.2642	1.23	.3907	1.74	.4591	2.25	.4878	2.76	.4971
.22	.0871	.73	.2673	1.24	.3925	1.75	.4599	2.26	.4881	2.77	.4972
.23	.0910	.74	.2704	1.25	.3944	1.76	.4608	2.27	.4884	2.78	.4973
.24	.0948	.75	.2734	1.26	.3962	1.77	.4616	2.28	.4887	2.79	.4974
.25	.0987	.76	.2764	1.27	.3980	1.78	.4625	2.29	.4890	2.80	.4974
.26	.0126	.77	.2794	1.28	.3997	1.79	.4633	2.30	.4893	2.81	.4975
.27	.1064	.78	.2823	1.29	.4015	1.80	.4641	2.31	.4896	2.82	.4976
.28	.1103	.79	.2852	1.30	.4032	1.81	.4649	2.32	.4898	2.83	.4977
.29	.1141	.80	.2881	1.31	.4049	1.82	.4656	2.33	.4901	2.84	.4977
.30	.1179	.81	.2910	1.32	.4006	1.83	.4664	2.34	.4904	2.85	.4978
.31	.1217	.82	.2939	1.33	.4082	1.84	.4671	2.35	.4906	2.86	.4979
.32	.1255	.83	.2967	1.34	.4099	1.85	.4678	2.36	.4909	2.87	.4979
.33	.1293	.84	.2995	1.35	.4115	1.86	.4686	2.37	.4911	2.88	.4980
.34	.1331	.85	.3023	1.36	.4131	1.87	.4693	2.38	.4913	2.89	.4981
.35	.1368	.86	.3051	1.37	.4147	1.88	.4699	2.39	.4916	2.90	.4981
.36	.1406	.87	.3078	1.38	.4162	1.89	.4706	2.40	.4917	2.91	.4982
.37	.1443	.88	.3106	1.39	.4177	1.90	.4713	2.41	.4920	2.92	.4982
.38	.1480	.89	.3133	1.40	.4192	1.91	.4719	2.42	.4922	2.93	.4983
.39	.1517	.90	.3159	1.41	.4207	1.92	.4726	2.43	.4925	2.94	.4984
.40	.1554	.91	.3186	1.42	.4222	1.93	.4732	2.44	.4927	2.95	.4984
.41	.1591	.92	.3212	1.43	.4236	1.94	.4738	2.45	.4929	2.96	.4985
.42	.1628	.93	.3238	1.44	.4251	1.95	.4744	2.46	.4931	2.97	.4985
.43	.1664	.94	.3264	1.45	.4265	1.96	.4750	2.47	.4932	2.98	.4986
.44	.1700	.95	.3289	1.46	.4279	1.97	.4756	2.48	.4934	2.99	.4986
.45	.1736	.96	.3315	1.47	.4292	1.98	.4761	2.49	.4936	3.00	.4987
.46	.1772	.97	.3340	1.48	.4306	1.99	.4767	2.50	.4938	3.20	.4993
.47	.1808	.98	.3365	1.49	.4319	2.00	.4772	2.51	.4940	3.40	.4997
.48	.1855	.99	.3389	1.50	.4332	2.01	.4778	2.52	.4941	3.60	.4997
.49	.1879	1.00	.3413	1.51	.4345	2.02	.4783	2.53	.4943	4.00	.499968
.50	.1915	1.01	.3438	1.52	.4357	2.03	.4788	2.54	.4945	4.50	.49997

Selected Bibliography

Berry, Donald A. and Bernard W. Lindgren. *Statistics, Theory and Methods.* Brooks/Cole Publishing Company. 1990

Campbell, Neil. *Biology* 3rd Edition. The Benjamin Cummings Publishing Company, Inc. 1993

Fruit Fly Chromosomes (*Drosophila melanogaster*) "The Genome Maps," *Science*, 254, 247-252, October 11, 1991

Hays, Leslie, SENSI, 1997.

Landwehr, James M. and Ann E. Watkins. *Exploring Data.* Dale Seymour Publications. 1987.

O'Brien, Stephen J., and Michael Dean. "In Search of AIDS-Resistance Genes," *Scientific American.* September, 1997.

Gardner, Eldon. *Principles of Genetics* 5th Edition. John Wiley and Sons, Inc. 1975

Rodecker, Stephen B. and Maryanna Quon-Warner. *Laboratory Experiments and Activities in Physical Science.* Spectrum Publications. 1992

Ward, John F. et al., "DNA Lesions Produced by Ionizing Radiation: Locally Multiply Damaged Sites," *Ionizing Radiation Damage to DNA: Molecular Aspects.* Wiley Liss, Inc. 1990

Ward, John. and Kuo, I., "Deoxynucleotides- Models for Studying Mechanisms of Strand Breakage in DNA," *International Journal of Radiation Biology*, Vol. 23, No. 6, December, 1973.

About the Authors

Steve Rodecker (M.A. German, M.S. Biology) has been active at all levels of science education for 20 years. Since 1985 he has taught biology, A.P. biology, and computer animation in science at Chula Vista High School in Chula Vista, California. He has written numerous articles on science education and another laboratory text entitled, *"Laboratory Experiments and Activities in Physical Science."* He has received several grants--including TAPESTRY, TAAP, GTE, and DOE--made numerous local, state, and national presentations on science methods, and in 1995 was awarded Disney's The American Teacher Awards "Nation's Outstanding Science Teacher." Currently he is a Science Specialist and Biology teacher with the Sweetwater Union High School District (2004).

Jim Patzold (B.S. Biology) has been teaching science for 30 years to all levels of students and teachers. He has been an instructor for the California Technology Project and has served as Assistant Director emeritus for the California Science Project. Currently he is an Assistant Principal at Clairemont High School in San Diego, California.